Meteorology

Albert Miller

San Jose State College

CHARLES E. MERRILL BOOKS, INC., COLUMBUS, OHIO

Merrill Physical Science Series

Robert J. Foster and **Walter A. Gong,** *Editors*

San Jose State College

Library of Congress Catalog Card Number: 66-18750

PRINTED IN THE UNITED STATES OF AMERICA

Editors' Foreword

As curricula become more crowded in this age of rapidly expanding knowledge and specialization, more and more colleges and universities are turning to integrated interdisciplinary courses to transmit the basic essentials of science to non-science majors. We believe that the rigid structure of most physical science textbooks has imposed severe limitations on instruction in these courses. Far too often, instructors trained in various specialities have had to attempt to fit the wide range of goals, abilities, and backgrounds of their students to a textbook, when the converse, of course, would be much more satisfactory.

In January, 1965, the editors, five authors, and representatives of Charles E. Merrill Books, Inc., met in San Francisco to implement a new conception of physical science textbooks. The result is the *Physical Science Series,* a collection of specially written, integrated materials in short, paperback form for the college physical science program. Our coordinated efforts were directed by three vital principles.

1. The Series permits maximum flexibility of use by instructors and students. Each paperback textbook represents a five-to-seven-week section of instruction, and may be used in any sequence or combination desired by the instructor. In addition, freedom of sequence within a single book is possible. This flexibility is especially helpful in courses that include laboratory experience. In this way it is hoped that each instructor will be free to choose the most appropriate materials for his students.

2. The subject areas are portrayed in a valid manner. Each book is written by a specialist in a different discipline—physicist, chemist, astronomer, meteorologist, geologist, and science educator. Thus, in place of a homogeneous blend of textbook statements, the individual paperback textbooks have distinctive scientific flavors. The student can discover both the contrasts and underlying unities in the viewpoints of scientists in different disciplines; he can, for example, compare the approach of the physicist, who performs lab-

iii

oratory experiments, with that of the geologist, who depends largely on observations of natural occurrences.

3. Scientific communication is clear, concise, and correct. Each author is both academician and experienced teacher. He has designed instruction around carefully selected scientific principles logically related to laws, definitions, and associated phenomena. Technology is used to provide illustrative examples rather than a myriad of facts to be remembered. Mathematical reasoning is used only when the sciences are made more (not less) understandable for the non-science major. Scientific jargon and excessive nomenclature are avoided.

San Jose, California   *Robert J. Foster*

Walter A. Gong

Table of Contents

INTRODUCTION

Weather is probably the subject of more daily conversation than any other of the physical sciences. Its popularity is certainly warranted: Like a fish in the ocean, man is confined to a very shallow layer of atmosphere; his physical and psychological state—indeed, his very life—depends on his atmospheric environment.

Aside from the use of its constituents in biological processes, the atmosphere controls life in many ways. It acts as an umbrella or shield, filtering various types of electromagnetic radiation and high-energy particles from the sun and space. Most meteorites are burned up before they can penetrate to the earth's surface. The winds transport heat and moisture and, in the process, by mixing the air, create more uniform conditions on the earth than would otherwise exist. The same winds drive the ocean currents, produce waves, erode the soil, and transport pollen and insects. Weather destroys man's structures and disrupts his systems of communication and transportation. The sounds he hears, the scents he smells, and the sights he sees are all affected by the state of the atmosphere. In fact, man and his activities are so delicately tuned to his atmospheric environment that he can tolerate very little change.

Like most sciences, *meteorology* attempts to establish the physical laws or relationships that describe the state of the atmosphere. From these, three practical advantages can be envisioned: (1) prediction of future weather to guide the planning of man's activities, (2) adaptation of man's activities to the weather, and (3) modification of weather. The most widely used of these applications is the first. But climatologists and agriculturists have long been concerned with the second. The third, weather modification, has received sporadic, generally minor attention until recently, when attempts to increase rainfall by cloud seeding have renewed interest among both laymen and professional meteorologists.

Prediction is a fundamental task of all sciences. Yet, despite over a hundred years of public weather forecasting, forecasts are still the subject of countless jokes. For a period of up to one or two days, the accuracy of weather forecasts is high—though certainly not perfect—and beyond a couple of days, the reliability falls off markedly. Yet meteorologists deal with the same kind of materials and laws used by other physical scientists. If the astronomer can forecast an eclipse years ahead without a miss, why can't the meteorologist, who has the same basic physical laws at his command, foretell exactly when tomorrow's rain will begin?

Hopefully, the answer to this question will become clear in this book.

1

The laws of physics can be applied to the atmosphere to explain its state. But the "state" of the atmosphere, or "weather," is a composite of many elements and these elements can be distributed in an infinite number of patterns in space and time. Even the layman describes weather by dozens of adjectives, such as rainy, foggy, cold, hot, windy, calm, damp, dry, etc.

The complexity of the weather patterns is so great that some meteorologists wonder whether it ever will be possible to completely describe the state of the atmosphere, let alone forecast its future condition in detail. The motions of the atmosphere are composed of convective "cells" and vortices (whirlpools) of many sizes, one superimposed on another. The "chaotic" appearance of a lake or ocean waves on a windy day would be more than equalled in the atmosphere, if air motions could be seen. Yet each whirl plays a role in the total weather picture. It is perhaps not surprising that progress in imposing "order" on the atmosphere so that its behavior can be predicted has been painfully slow.

After the introductory chapter, which deals with the general properties of the atmosphere and measurements, two basic concepts are employed in the discussion of atmospheric processes. One is that the atmosphere is a giant *heat engine*. An engine is a gadget that transforms energy from one type to another. In the atmosphere, radiant energy from the sun is transformed to heat. Because the heat energy of the atmosphere varies from place to place, some of it is changed into kinetic energy, i.e., energy of motion. Man-made engines work the same way, of course. If the gases in the cylinder of a gasoline engine were not hotter than those on the outside, the pistons would not move. Examination of the ways in which different energy levels are created within the atmosphere is a convenient way to decipher the complex processes.

The other concept employed in this book is that atmospheric processes and motions exist in a large range of sizes or *scales*. In the case of air motion, for example, there exists a hierarchy of flow systems that range from giant "eddies" that may cover 10% or more of the area of the globe to the tiny whirls that scatter the dust on a road. Although there is an interplay between each size and its smaller and bigger "brothers," they differ from one another in their characteristics of air motion and weather, and in the relative significance of the various atmospheric forces. For example, the circulation pattern of a middle latitude cyclone has a horizontal dimension about a hundred times that of its vertical extent, but in a thunderstorm the depth is about the same as the width. In the case of the cyclone, the earth's rotation is a significant factor in determining the flow, but not so in the case of the thunderstorm convective cell.

The discussion of atmospheric processes and weather prediction requires so much space that the interesting applications of man's adaptation and weather modification can only be touched on briefly in this book. Except for cloud seeding, which is covered in the portion of the first chapter that deals with the properties of clouds and precipitation, these topics are left to the final chapter.

Chapter 1

The Atmosphere

PROPERTIES OF THE ATMOSPHERE

Composition

The shell of air that surrounds the earth is a mechanical mixture of many gases in which are suspended, in quite variable amounts, particles of liquid and solid matter. The gas molecules are free to move about, although gravitational attraction prevents them from escaping the earth. Temperature is a measure of molecular motion and gravitational attraction depends on the massiveness of a body; it follows that small, hot bodies, such as the planet Mercury, can hold only the heaviest gas molecules. Earth is massive enough, yet cool enough, to retain a thin envelope of gases that plays an intricate but very significant role in life processes.

A summary of what is now known about the composition of the atmosphere is presented in Fig. 1-1. Below 80 km the gases of the atmosphere are relatively well mixed. In this layer, known as the *homosphere*, the proportion of each constituent gas, with few exceptions, is fairly constant throughout. In contrast, in the *heterosphere*, above 80 km, the various gases have tended to stratify in accordance with their weights, as occurs with liquids of different densities.

In a sample of dry "pure" air in the homosphere, nitrogen occupies about 78 per cent of the volume, oxygen about 21 per cent, argon almost 1 per cent, carbon dioxide only about 0.03 per cent, and a host of other gases such as neon, helium, methane, krypton, xenon, hydrogen, and ozone together comprise only a hundredth of 1 per cent. The chemical properties of these gases are of considerable interest to the biologist since some, such as nitrogen, oxygen, and carbon dioxide, are involved in life processes. However, the flow of gases into and out of organisms is so slow that it has little effect on the concentration of gases in the atmosphere, and the meteorologist does not normally concern himself with them. Carbon dioxide and ozone are exceptions. As will be explained later, both of these gases play a role in the energy balance of the earth and its atmosphere. Due to differences in rates of pro-

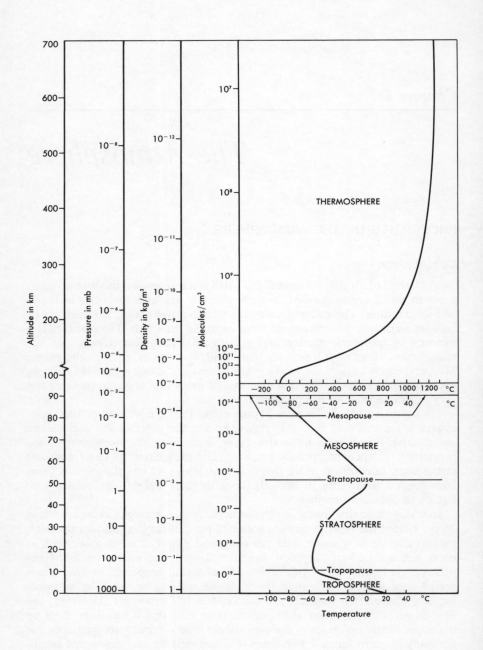

Fig. 1-1. **Vertical distribution of atmospheric properties and phenomena.**

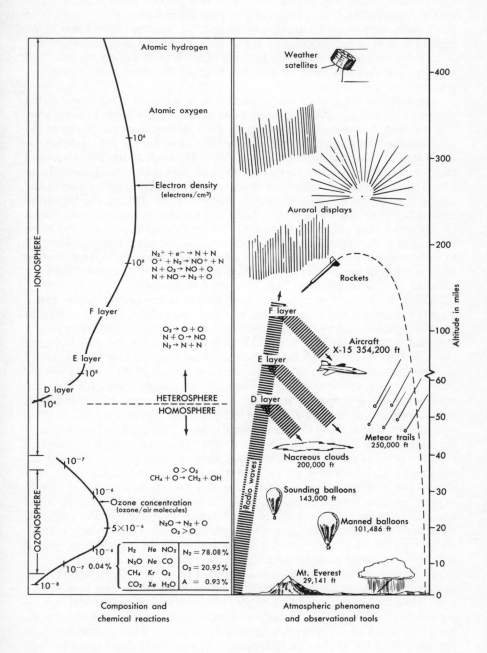

Atomic hydrogen

Weather satellites

Atomic oxygen

10^6

← Electron density
(electrons/cm³)

IONOSPHERE

Auroral displays

$N_2^+ + e^- \rightarrow N + N$
$O^+ + N_2 \rightarrow NO^+ + N$
$N + O_2 \rightarrow NO + O$
$N + NO \rightarrow N_2 + O$

10^6

Rockets

F layer

F layer

$O_2 \rightarrow O + O$
$N + O \rightarrow NO$
$N_2 \rightarrow N + N$

Aircraft
X-15 354,200 ft

E layer
10^5

E layer

D layer
10^4

HETEROSPHERE
HOMOSPHERE

D layer

Meteor trails
250,000 ft

10^{-7}

Nacreous clouds
200,000 ft

OZONOSPHERE

$O > O_3$
$CH_4 + O \rightarrow CH_3 + OH$

10^{-6}

← Ozone concentration
(ozone/air molecules)

Radio waves

Sounding balloons
143,000 ft

5×10^{-6}

$N_2O \rightarrow N_2 + O$
$O_3 > O$

Manned balloons
101,486 ft

10^{-6} 0.04%

10^{-7} 0.04%

H_2	He	NO_2	$N_2 = 78.08\%$
N_2O	Ne	CO	$O_2 = 20.95\%$
CH_4	Kr	O_3	
CO_2	Xe	H_2O	$A = 0.93\%$

Mt. Everest
29,141 ft

10^{-8}

Altitude in miles

-400

-300

-200

-100

-60

-50

-40

-30

-20

-10

-0

Composition and
chemical reactions

Atmospheric phenomena
and observational tools

duction and absorption, the amount of carbon dioxide from place to place varies considerably. Thus, for example, over cities where great amounts of fossil fuels such as coal and oil are burned, the concentration tends to be high. There is some speculation that the average CO_2 concentration has been rising due to the increased burning of such fuels during the past half century, and that this increase may be changing the atmosphere's heat balance.

Air is never completely dry or pure. There is always some water in the gaseous state and sometimes it occupies as much as 4 per cent of the volume. The amount, however, varies greatly in both time and space. Water is the only substance that can exist in all three states—gas, liquid, and solid—at the temperatures that exist normally on the earth. The cycle of transition between these states goes on continuously and plays an important role in maintaining life. But, in addition, these *phase changes* of water play another role in the atmosphere which is significant to the meteorologist: During the transition from a liquid or solid to a vapor state, water molecules take up some heat energy which they obtain from the air in which they are contained, and when they revert to the liquid or solid state they release the same amount of energy to their environment. Thus, heat consumed at one place during evaporation may be released at an entirely different place during condensation. This is an effective way of transporting heat over great distances.

Ozone is found in very minute quantities near the surface of the earth, usually comprising less than one part in a hundred million. If all the ozone in the atmosphere could be brought down to sea level pressure and temperature, it would form a layer only about 2.5 mm thick. As can be seen from the curve of Fig. 1-1, although the concentration of ozone is low at all levels of the atmosphere, there is a sharp peak near the altitude of 30 km. Despite the small quantities, ozone is quite significant in the radiant energy transfer that goes on in the atmosphere. Because of its strong absorption of ultraviolet light from the sun, very little of these lethal wavelengths arrive at the surface of the earth. The ozone (O_3) of the atmosphere is believed to form when an atom of oxygen (O), a molecule of oxygen (O_2), and a third, "catalytic" particle, such as nitrogen, collide. The atomic oxygen is formed in the atmosphere by the splitting of molecular oxygen under the action of very short wave solar radiation; note from Fig. 1-1 that the production of atomic oxygen becomes especially prominent in the heterosphere. The maximum of · ozone near 30 km is apparently due to a balance of two factors: the availability of very short wave solar energy to produce atomic oxygen, which is gradually depleted as it traverses the upper layers of the atmosphere, and a sufficient density of particles to bring about the collisions required.

A variety of solid particles are suspended in the air. These include fine dust particles swept up by the wind from exposed soils; soot from forest fires, industrial fires, industrial plants, and volcanoes; pollen and microorganisms lifted by the wind; meteoritic dust; and salts injected into the atmosphere when ocean spray is evaporated. Large particles are too heavy to remain long in the air, but there are many, so small that they cannot be seen individually with the naked eye, that remain suspended for months or even years. The minute particles of dust thrown high into the atmosphere by the violent eruption of the volcano Krakatoa in the East Indies in 1883 circled the globe for at least two years. The number of non-gaseous particles of all types in the atmosphere is extremely variable, ranging from only a few hundred per cubic centimeter in very clean air to several million per cubic centimeter in smoke-laden air. The average over cities is about 150,000/cm³.

All of these solid particles in the air are frequently referred to as "dust." The presence of dust in the atmosphere is important not only because it influences the transparency of the air. Without it, there could be no appreciable condensation. Certain types of dust, particularly the salts, are *hygroscopic,* i.e., they attract water. These hygroscopic nuclei permit condensation to occur when the concentration of water vapor in the air is relatively low.

The separation of gases according to their molecular weight begins to become evident in the heterosphere. Even more significant is the fact that a large part of the air consists of electrically charged particles. This electrification is produced by the intense shortwave (ultraviolet and X) radiations of the sun that are absorbed by the air particles. In the process, atoms and molecules have electrons stripped from them, thus producing free electrons and positively charged particles. The rate of ion production will depend, of course, on the density of molecules and atoms available for ionization and the intensity of the radiation; the first will decrease, while the second will increase with increasing height above the earth's surface. The capture of electrons by positively charged ions will also depend on the density of air, since the likelihood of collisions is greater if the particles are crowded than if they have a lot of room. As a result of a combination of these factors, there is a maximum of free electrons at about 350 km, although the distribution is rather complicated, forming into layers.

This electrically charged portion of the atmosphere, known as the *ionosphere*, is very useful for radio communications, since it reflects radio waves. Around-the-world transmissions are accomplished by bouncing radio waves, which move in straight lines, between the ionosphere and the earth's surface.

The distribution of electron density with height is not constant. There is a diurnal variation in the strength of some layers due to changes in the intensity of solar radiation. In addition, there are occasional *sudden ionospheric disturbances* (*S.I.D.*, as they are called) and "ionospheric storms" that are associated with disturbances on the sun. The S.I.D. lasts for 15 to 30 minutes, and is produced by bursts of ultraviolet energy from the sun that causes a sudden increase in the production of electrons. Since electrons absorb part of the radio energy that strikes them, a sudden increase in their number may actually smother the radio energy, leading to "fadeouts" of communications on the sunlit side of the earth. Ionospheric storms, which can occur during the day or night and last for hours or even days, are believed to be caused by a stream of charged particles emitted from the sun. These fast-moving particles, guided toward the poles by the earth's magnetic field, not only ionize the air; they also produce the beautiful displays of aurora borealis ("northern lights") and aurora australis ("southern lights").

Temperature

The mean vertical temperature distribution shown on the left in Fig. 1-1 is still another basis for dividing the atmosphere into shells or layers. In the lowest of these layers, the *troposphere,* the temperature decreases with height, on the average, at the rate of 6.5°C/km (3½ °F/1,000 ft). In this layer, vertical convection currents, induced primarily by the uneven heating of the layer by the earth's surface, keep the air fairly well stirred. Practically all clouds and weather, and most of the dust and water vapor of the atmosphere are found in this turbulent layer. Its upper boundary, called the *tropopause,* is at an average elevation of about 10 km, but varies with time of year and latitude, and even from day to day at the same place. Typically, the tropopause is at an elevation of 15 or 16 km over the equator and only 5 or 6 km over the polar regions. It tends to be higher in summer than in winter.

In the *stratosphere,* whose upper boundary lies at about 50 km, the temperature is first constant. Then it increases with height, reaching a temperature at the *stratopause* which is not much cooler than at sea level. The clouds and the vertical convection currents of air formed near the earth's surface do not usually penetrate very far into the stratosphere. The air in this layer is dry. The increasing temperature with height can be explained by the absorption of shortwave radiation by ozone.

The *mesosphere* is the zone between 50 and 85 km in which the temperature decreases rapidly with height, reaching about −95°C at the *mesopause,* which is the coldest point in the atmosphere. Strong vertical convection probably exists in the mesosphere.

Above the mesosphere, the temperature increases rapidly at first, and then more slowly, with height. This hot layer is known as the *thermosphere.* At heights above 500-600 km, the density of particles is so low that collisions among them are infrequent and some of the particles can escape the gravitational pull of the earth. This zone, which marks a transition from the earth's atmosphere to the very thin interplanetary gas beyond, is called the *exosphere.*

Characteristics of Gases

There are three states in which matter exists: solid, liquid, and gas. Almost all substances on the earth occur naturally in only a single state. The gross characteristics of each of the three states are quite familiar: Solids resist changes in their shape and do not flow, while liquids and gases are easily deformed and do flow (and thus are known as *fluids*); the space occupied by a solid or a liquid is not easily altered, but a gas spreads out to fill the entire volume available to it (we say that gases are *compressible*). These characteristics can be explained largely in terms of how closely bound are the molecules of the substance: In a solid, the molecules are locked into position and their motion is restricted to oscillations over short distances from their mean positions; the molecules in a liquid have considerable freedom of movement, but they are bound to the bulk of the liquid with sufficient force so that they cannot significantly increase the mean distance between individual molecules; in a gas, the *adhesion* between molecules is weak, the molecules are relatively far apart, and they can move about with comparative freedom throughout the volume occupied by the gas.

We shall be concerned primarily with the "gross" properties, particularly those of gases. Although we may occasionally mention molecules and atoms in the way of explanation, we shall be interested primarily in populations of molecules and atoms and how they behave as groups.

One such gross property of a gas is the space that a given number of gas particles may occupy. At sea level there are about 25×10^{18} molecules* of air in each cubic centimeter (about the volume of the tip of your small finger up to the base of the nail). The number of molecules per unit volume (25×10^{18} *molecules*/cm^3 at sea level), is referred to as the molecular *density* of the gas. More commonly we refer to the total mass of the molecules, rather than their number, and the density can then be stated as the number of grams contained in each cubic centimeter. Near sea level, 1 cm^3 of air contains a mass of about 1.2×10^{-3} g (0.0012 g), so that the density is 1.2×10^{-3} g/cm^3.

Another bulk property of fluids is *pressure,* which is defined as the force per unit area exerted on any surface being bombarded by the fluid's moving molecules. Held to the earth by gravitational attraction, the earth's atmosphere has a cumulative force or weight per unit area averaging 14.7 lb/in.² at mean sea level. In the cgs system of units, the standard sea level pressure is 1,013,250 dynes/cm^2. Since the dyne/cm^2 is such a small and "wordy" unit, the "bar," which is equal to a million dynes/cm^2, has been introduced as a pressure unit. For meteorological purposes, the *millibar* (abbreviated mb and equal to 1/1,000 bar) is most widely used. The pressure of one standard atmosphere is thus 1,013.25 mb.

Gases are easily compressed, a fact that is illustrated by the pressure distribution with height given in Fig. 1-1 and in the table of Appendix 3. In water, the pressure increases almost exactly in proportion with depth below the water surface, but not so in the atmosphere. As can be seen from the table, one must ascend 2,500 m for the pressure to fall off 25 per cent (about 250 mb) from its sea level value, but over 3,000 m more for another 25 per cent drop, and another 5,000 m for an additional 25 per cent; in the layer between sea level and 5,500 m, the pressure decreases 518 mb, but in the layer between 30,000 m and 35,000 m, the decrease is less than 3 mb. Evidently the air near the bottom of the atmosphere is compressed by the weight of the air resting above. This compressibility characteristic of gases is of great significance in atmospheric processes. As will be pointed out in a later chapter, rapid compressions and expansions of air occur naturally in the atmosphere, and these are largely responsible for much of the weather.

Gas Laws

We remind the reader of two fundamental laws about the behavior of gases. These relate the properties of temperature, density (or volume), and

---

* The molecule itself has a volume of only about 6×10^{-24} cm^3, so that the "open" space is about 10,000 times greater than the "occupied" space.

pressure. (1) *Boyle's law* states that, if the temperature of a gas does not change, its density varies directly as the pressure varies. In symbolic form, $p \propto d$, or $p = kd$, where p is the value of the pressure, d is the density, and k is a constant. (2) *Charles' law* states that if the pressure within a gas is kept unchanged, its volume will change in proportion to any temperature change that may occur. This means that, for a fixed amount of mass, the density (mass per volume) is inversely proportional to the temperature, when the pressure is constant; i.e., the density decreases when the temperature increases, and it increases when the temperature decreases. In other words, at the same pressure, cold air is more dense than warm air.

OBSERVATIONS OF THE ATMOSPHERE

Weather observations of a sort have been made by man since earliest times, but systematic measurements of the elements did not begin until the invention of instruments during the 17th and 18th centuries. Until the 20th century, measurements were confined to the air close to the ground. Systematic measurements of most of the earth's atmosphere are scanty even today.

A complete description of the physical state of the atmosphere requires the measurement of dozens of quantities. Some variables, such as temperature, pressure, wind, and humidity, have the greatest applications to weather forecasting and are therefore most widely measured; others, such as the concentration of certain gases, dusts, and electric charge, are of more limited interest. We will deal with those quantities most commonly measured by the meteorologist.

Measurement of the state of the atmosphere is quite difficult. In addition to the usual requirement that an instrument measure accurately whatever it is designed to measure, the meteorological instrument must be rugged enough to withstand the weather elements—the force of buffeting winds, the corrosive action of high humidity and flying dust, the extremes of heat and cold. Another difficulty is the inaccessibility of much of the atmosphere, so that instruments must be built to transmit their measurements to distant ground points; they must be rugged and light enough to be carried aloft by balloons and rockets and cheap enough so they can be used in the large quantities necessary to observe the atmosphere. Finally, meteorological measurements must be "representative," a difficult objective to achieve, considering the enormous size of the atmosphere and the comparatively few observations that can be made. Taking the depth of water in a single 8-in. diameter rain gauge as representative of the average rainfall over an area of many square miles is somewhat like assuming that the height of a single student taken at random is equal to the average of the entire school.

Temperature

A thermometer is a device that measures the degree of hotness or coldness of a body on a numerical scale. This is usually done by correlating physical changes in the thermometer with temperature changes. Thus, for example, the increase in volume of mercury with increased temperature is used in the common mercury-in-glass thermometer. Another way to measure the temperature of a body is to relate changes in the properties of the body itself with changes in its temperature. The color of steel in a furnace is a good index of its temperature; the speed at which sound waves travel through air depends on the air temperature.

Almost every type of temperature measuring device has been used in meteorology, but the expansion type is the most commonly used for observation near the surface of the earth, because of its ruggedness and cheapness. The ordinary liquid-in-glass thermometer is widely used in meteorology. Liquid-in-glass thermometers that will register the maximum or minimum temperature during a period require slight modifications. The maximum thermometer has a constriction of the bore of the glass tube just above the bulb; as the temperature rises, the mercury is forced through the constriction, but when the temperature falls the weight of the mercury in the column is insufficient to reunite it with that in the bore, so that the top of the mercury column indicates the highest point reached. The maximum thermometer can be reset by shaking the thermometer, thereby forcing the mercury through the constriction.

The minimum thermometer contains alcohol in the bore, with a small, dumbbell-shaped glass index placed inside the column of alcohol. The index is kept just below the meniscus of the alcohol column by surface tension. With the thermometer mounted horizontally, when the alcohol contracts, the meniscus drags the index with it; but when the alcohol expands, the meniscus advances, leaving the index at its lowest point. To reset, the index can be returned to the meniscus by merely tilting the thermometer.

Expansion-type thermometers are also used for recording the temperature. Either a bimetal or a Bourdon thermometer is used to move a pen arm that traces its position on a paper chart driven by a clock. The bimetal thermometer is the type ordinarily used in thermostatic control devices. Two strips of metal, having different rates of expansion during a temperature change, are welded and rolled together. The difference in expansion of the two strips causes changes in the curvature of the element as the temperature changes; with one end fixed in position, the other end is free to move the pen arm and indicate the temperature. The Bourdon thermometer consists of a flat, curved metal tube containing a liquid; as the volume of the liquid changes with temperature, the curvature of the tube changes and this can be used to move the pen arm in a fashion similar to that of the bimetallic strip.

The principal use of electrical thermometers in meteorology is in the radiosonde, which is attached to a balloon and transmits temperature, pressure, and humidity data by radio as it ascends through the atmosphere. There are two general types of electrical thermometers: (1) the thermoelectric thermometer, which operates on the principle that temperature differences among the junctions of two or more different metal wires in a circuit will induce a flow of electricity; (2) the resistance thermometer, which is based on the principle that the resistance to the flow of electricity in a substance depends on its temperature. It is the latter that is used in the radiosonde. The ceramic elements commonly used are called thermistors.

Measurement of temperature

Obtaining meaningful air temperatures is not a simple procedure. Air is a poor conductor of heat and quite transparent to radiation, especially in the short wavelengths emitted by the sun. That this is so is quite evident when one moves a few feet from the shade into the sun; even though the air temperature is almost identical, one feels much warmer in the sun. Or, standing near a fire, the side of the person facing the fire "roasts" while the other side "freezes."

Most thermometers are much better radiation absorbers than air. They absorb energy from the sun and other warm objects that passes right through the air. If the thermometer is to measure the air temperature, such radiation must be prevented from reaching the thermometer. This is accomplished by shielding the thermometer, at the same time keeping it in contact with the air. This can be done by enclosing the thermometer within a highly polished tube, allowing plenty of room for air to circulate past the thermometer. However, when several temperature measuring devices are used, it is convenient to house them in a special "instrument shelter," which permits air to pass through. The shelter also serves to keep the instruments dry during rain, since a wet thermometer will generally read lower than a dry one. (See the section on humidity.)

The thermometer should be ventilated artificially when there is little wind, because the conductivity of air is poor ("dead," or stagnant, air is often used for insulation) and the thin layer that encases the thermometer might have a different temperature than the "free" air. By stirring the air, this layer is mixed with the surrounding air.

Even if the precautions in measuring temperature given above are taken, there is still the question of how to interpret temperature measurements. On a sunny, windless day the temperature of air within an inch or two of a cement sidewalk can be 30°F or more higher than at the 4-ft level. Even at the same height above the ground the temperature differs greatly between the city and the country, within forests and over open land, along sloping land and flat land. Differences in the thermometer environment are so important that measurements at a single point can rarely be considered representative of the average conditions closer than 2°F.

Pressure

Pressure is defined as the force per unit area exerted on any surface in a fluid. The orientation of the surface will not affect the pressure. In the case of the atmosphere, which has no outer walls to confine its volume, the pressure exerted at any level is due almost entirely to the weight of the air pressing down from above; i.e., the force results from gravitational attraction. (The units of pressure were given in the section on characteristics of gases.)

As would be expected from the discussion in the last paragraph, the pressure changes most rapidly in the vertical. In the lowest few kilometers, the pressure decrease amounts to about 1 mb per 10 m (1 in. Hg/1,000 ft). Because of the compressibility of air, the rate at which the pressure decreases with height becomes slower at greater heights.

Variations of pressure in the horizontal are much smaller than they are in the vertical. Near sea level, the change of pressure with distance rarely exceeds 3 mb per 100 km (3×10^{-4} mb/10 m, or 5 mb/100 miles) and is usually much less than half this rate. The horizontal variations in pressure, although small, are able to produce the winds we observe. Since pressure measures the weight per unit area of the atmosphere, variations in pressure along any horizontal surface (such as sea level) must arise through variations in the average density of the atmosphere; i.e., there must be more molecules in a column of air above a point having high pressure than in one above a point where low pressure is observed.

Pressure also changes with time at a single place. Some of these changes are of an irregular nature, caused by occasional invasions of air having a different mean density. But there is also a quite regular diurnal oscillation of the pressure that causes, on the average, two peaks (at about 10 A.M. and 10 P.M.) and two minima (at about 4 A.M. and 4 P.M.). The difference between maxima and minima is greatest near the equator (up to 3 mb), decreasing to practically zero in the polar regions. These regular fluctuations in the pressure are analogous to the tidal motions in the ocean, but in the case of the ocean it is the gravitational pull of the moon and sun that causes the water surface to bulge slightly outward from the earth, while in the atmosphere the daily heating and cooling cycle appears to be the dominant cause of the pressure variations. Diurnal wind oscillations accompany the migration of these maxima and minima of pressure around the earth each day; these are hardly detectable at low elevations in the atmosphere, but become quite strong between 80 and 100 km.

Measurement of Pressure

The mercurial barometer, invented by Torricelli in 1643, is still the fundamental instrument for measuring atmospheric pressure. It is constructed by filling a tube measuring about 33 in. in length with mercury. The mercury in the tube will flow into the dish until the column of mercury is about 30 in. high (at a sea level site), leaving a vacuum at the top.

In principle, the barometer is merely a weighing balance (Fig. 1-2), the pressure exerted by the atmosphere on the exposed surface of the mercury in the dish equaling that exerted by the mercury in the tube. Changes in atmospheric pressure are detected from changes in the height of the column of mercury. Although it is now the custom to use the height of the column as a pressure unit (millimeters or inches of mercury), conversion to such units as dynes/cm², mb, or lb/in.², can be made as follows:

The density of Hg at 0°C is 13.6 g/cm³. (Note that the height of the column of mercury will depend on temperature as well as pressure, since mercury expands with increased temperature. To obtain the true pressure,

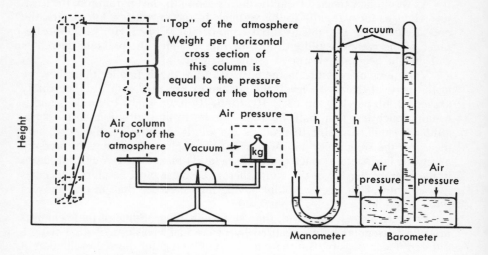

The pressure in the atmosphere at any point is the result of the
weight of the air above the point.

Fig. 1-2.   "Weighing" the atmosphere—principle of the barometer.

one must correct for this mercury expansion.) The mass of a column of
mercury = mercury density × volume = density × height × cross-sectional
area of tube; its *weight*, therefore, would be obtained by multiplying by the
acceleration of gravity (weight = mass × gravity) and the weight per unit
area (pressure) exerted by the column obtained by dividing by the area.
Thus, pressure = gravity × density × height. For example, if the height of
the column of mercury were 76 cm, the pressure in dynes/cm² would be
$980.6 \times 13.6 \times 76 = 1.0136 \times 10^6$ dynes/cm² = 1,013.6 mb. Here the
value of 980.6 cm/sec/sec has been used for gravity; in practice the gravity
value of the particular place should be used.

The aneroid barometer, although not usually as accurate as the mercurial barometer, is more widely used because it is smaller, more portable,
usually cheaper to manufacture, and simpler to adapt to recording mechanisms. Its principle of operation is that of the spring balance (Fig. 1-3). A
thin metal chamber, with most of its air evacuated, is prevented from col-
lapsing under the force of atmospheric pressure by a spring. The force
exerted by a spring depends on the distance it is stretched. The balance between the spring force and the atmospheric force will thus depend on the
width of the chamber. Changes in this width can be discerned by movement
of an arm attached to one end of the chamber; these deflections are usually
magnified by levers. If a pen is attached to the arm, the instrument becomes
a barograph.

The altimeters used in aircraft and by mountain climbers, surveyors, and
others are usually nothing more than aneroid barometers, made to indicate

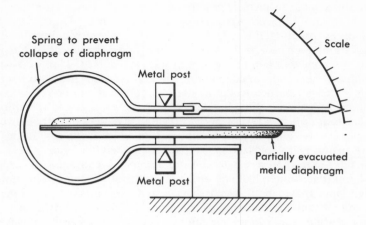

Fig. 1-3. **Principle of the aneroid barometer.**

altitude rather than pressure. They are designed to give the altitude for the standard ("normal") pressure distribution with height, and so will give slightly erroneous readings. For accurate determinations of altitude, the true density of the air for each altitude increment must be measured and corrections to the indicated altitude computed.

Humidity

The concentration of gaseous water in the atmosphere varies from practically zero to as much as 4 per cent (4 g of water in every 100 g of air). The extreme variability in the amount of water vapor, in both space and time, is due to water's rather unique ability to exist in all three states—gas, liquid, and solid—at the temperatures normally found on earth. Water vapor is continuously being extracted from the atmosphere through condensation (vapor to liquid) and sublimation (vapor to ice); some of this may fall to the earth through precipitation. Water is continuously being added to the atmosphere through evaporation (liquid to vapor) from the oceans, lakes, rivers, soil, plants, and raindrops, and sublimation (ice to vapor) from snow flakes, glaciers, etc.

The exact amount of water vapor that exists at any place and time is important to the meteorologist because of the role water plays in weather processes. It is significant, first of all, because condensation is an important aspect of "weather." Second, water vapor is the most important radiation absorber in the air and thus affects the energy balance of the atmosphere (Chap. 2). Third, the release of the latent heat of condensation is an important source of energy for the maintenance of atmospheric processes.

For a substance such as water to change its phase from solid to liquid or liquid to gas, the forces that bind the molecules together must be broken down. Work must be done in overcoming these intermolecular forces, so the molecules must expend part of their internal energy. The molecules acquire this energy from their environment. It is for this reason that skin is cooled by evaporation of perspiration, and water in a porous water bag is cooled by evaporation through the walls. The energy required to effect a "phase" or state change such as occurs in evaporation is called *latent heat* because it reappears when the change of state is reversed. Thus, to evaporate 1 g of liquid water, approximately 600 cal are required; if the same gram of gaseous water is returned to liquid state, the 600 cal will be released to the environment. A similar thing happens during the ice to liquid transition, but the *latent heat of fusion* is only about 80 cal/g. Changes directly between ice and vapor involve a latent heat of sublimation which is the sum of the latent heats of fusion and vaporization, i.e., approximately 680 cal.

We refer to the gaseous state of water as vapor because it is so easily condensed, but it acts much like any other gas in the atmosphere. The molecules of water vapor move about, occupy space, and exert pressure as do the other gases, except that the amounts of the other gases are relatively fixed. The quantity of water vapor in the air can be expressed in a variety of ways. One is the density of water vapor, usually referred to as the *absolute humidity* and expressed as the number of grams of water vapor in a given volume. Normally there are not more than about 12 g/m^3, although as much as 40 g/m^3 can occur.

The *partial pressure* of water vapor, i.e., the contribution made by water to the total atmospheric pressure, is another measure that can be used. It is usually expressed in millibars or inches of mercury. Typically, the water vapor pressure does not exceed 15 mb (0.44 in. Hg), although it can reach double or more this value.

The amount of water vapor that can be added to a volume at any given atmospheric pressure and temperature is limited. When a volume has reached its capacity for water vapor, it is said to be saturated and the volume will accept no more gaseous water. The *saturation vapor pressure*, as this maximum vapor pressure is called, is a function of temperature. (See Fig. 1-4. The first two columns of Table A of Appendix 2 also illustrate how the saturation vapor pressure varies with temperature near sea level.) This dependence of the saturation vapor pressure on the temperature is why cooling is so important in producing condensation. For example, if a sample of air having a temperature of 70°F and a water vapor pressure of 0.595 in. Hg were cooled to 45°F, the sample would become saturated at a temperature of 64°F and further cooling would result in condensation of the excess moisture; when the 45°F temperature was reached, the saturation vapor pressure would be only 0.298 in. Hg and so almost half of the vapor would have liquefied. The temperature to which a sample of air must be cooled (at constant atmospheric pressure) to make it "saturated" is called the *dew point*. In the above example, the dew point of the sample before condensation began was 64°F; after condensation begins the temperature and the dew point are equal. Thus, the dew point is a direct measure of the water vapor pressure; the difference between the temperature and the dew point is a measure of the degree of saturation of the air.

The *relative humidity* is the ratio of the actual vapor pressure to saturation vapor pressure, i.e., relative humidity = actual vapor pressure/saturation

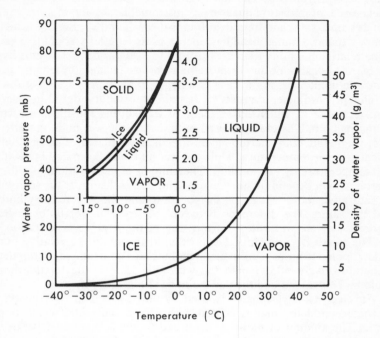

Fig. 1-4. **Saturation vapor pressure and density as a function of temperature. (Inset: variation below 0°C.)**

vapor pressure. The ratio is usually multiplied by 100 and expressed in per cent. Relative humidity measures how close the air is to saturation (100 per cent indicates complete saturation). In the example given above, the relative humidity before cooling was $(0.595/0.732) \times 100 = 81$ per cent; between 64°F and 45°F, the relative humidity remained constant at 100 per cent. The relative humidity is very sensitive to temperature change: there is normally a large diurnal change of relative humidity, even when the quantity of moisture in the air is constant, merely because the daily temperature variation continuously changes the saturation vapor pressure.

Measurement of Humidity

The most accurate way to measure humidity is to pass an air sample through a chemical drying agent that absorbs all of the water vapor, and then weigh the water collected. However, for meteorological observations, this procedure is not practical, since the sampling time is too long and the analytical tools are too complicated. Study of the atmosphere requires almost instantaneous sampling under field conditions.

None of the many techniques used to measure atmospheric humidity are completely satisfactory; here we will mention just a few of the most commonly used instruments. The hair hygrometer is probably the oldest and most widely used of moisture measuring instruments. Many organic materials such as wood, skin, and hair absorb moisture when the humidity is high, and so they expand. Human head hair increases its length by about 2½ per cent as the relative humidity increases from 0 to 100 per cent. The hair hygrometer merely consists of one or more hairs whose changes in length are made to move a pointer or, in the case of a hygrograph, a pen.

The psychrometer consists of a pair of ordinary liquid-in-glass thermometers, one of which has a piece of tight-fitting muslin cloth wrapped around its bulb. The cloth covered bulb, called the wet bulb, is wetted with pure water and both thermometers are then ventilated. The dry bulb will indicate the air temperature, while the wet bulb will be cooled below the dry bulb temperature by evaporation. The amount of evaporation, and therefore of cooling, will depend on how nearly saturated is the air. If the surroundings are saturated, there will be no evaporation, and the wet and dry bulbs will read the same. The difference between the dry and wet bulbs, called the *depression of the wet bulb*, is a measure of the degree of saturation of the air. The tables of Appendix 2 can be used to obtain the relative humidity or dew point from psychrometric readings. As an example, if the dry bulb temperature were 60.0°F and the wet bulb 55.0°F, the relative humidity would be 73 per cent and the dew point 51°F.

An electrical hygrometer is used in the radiosonde. It consists of an electrical conductor that is coated with lithium chloride, which is hygroscopic. The amount of moisture absorbed by the conductor depends on the relative humidity of the air, and the electrical resistance of the conductor is a function of its dampness.

Clouds and Precipitation

In the discussion on humidity, it was implied that as soon as the concentration of vapor begins to exceed the saturation value, which is largely dependent on temperature, the excess moisture becomes liquid or solid. It is not quite that simple. For condensation, sublimation, or freezing to occur there must be a suitable surface available. Dew or frost forms easily on grass, soil, windows, etc., whenever the air temperature reaches the dew point or the frost point. But in the free atmosphere there are no such extensive surfaces.

In pure air (i.e., all gas with no "foreign" particles, water droplets, or ice crystals) condensation or sublimation is extremely difficult to achieve, even under highly super-saturated conditions (relative humidity much greater than 100 per cent). For a single droplet to form, it would be necessary for many water molecules* in the air not only to collide with each other but to stick together. However, the probability of such multiple collisions is extremely small and even when some do stick, thermal agitation of the molecules tends to cause some of the outer molecules to escape from any small "embryo" that may form. Only after a droplet has reached a critical size are

---

* About 1,000 molecules are needed to form a droplet having a diameter of only 4×10^{-7} cm (the wavelength of X rays).

the binding forces sufficient to hold more of the molecules that strike its outer surface than the number that escape it. Since molecular speed depends on temperature, this critical size is a function of temperature. Once this critical size is reached, further growth is very possible, but the probability that the hundreds of millions of molecules required to produce such a size will not only collide but stick together is extremely small in pure air.

Fortunately, in the natural atmosphere there are numerous particles much larger than individual molecules that provide surfaces or *nuclei* to which water molecules can adhere. It is around these that water droplets and ice crystals grow. (Cloud and rain drops are never "pure," despite the myth that they are, although the proportion of "foreign" particles to water is usually very small.) Certain types of particles, such as salts injected into the atmosphere by the evaporation of sea spray, attract water molecules to their surfaces, and are said to be *hygroscopic nuclei.* On these, condensation may actually begin well before the air becomes saturated. However, salt nuclei represent only a small part of the total suspended in the air, and there are a large number of other types of particles, such as combustion products, meteoritic dust, and soil, that also serve as nuclei. These small particles, with diameters of up to 1 micron (a thousandth of a millimeter) and in quantities of 10,000 or more per cubic centimeter, are so small that they remain suspended in the air for days at a time.

Pure liquid water will not freeze without nuclei either, and there is evidence that certain materials are effective as freezing nuclei at warmer temperatures than others. In fairly large volumes of water, the likelihood of having at least a few effective nuclei is quite high and freezing normally occurs at a temperature very close to $0°C$. But in very small droplets, it is possible to achieve a temperature as low as $-40°C$ before freezing takes place. Indeed, in the atmosphere it is common for liquid water drops to exist in clouds at temperatures as low as $-20°C$. It has been found that large drops freeze at a higher temperature than small drops.

Fog and clouds are composed of liquid water and/or ice particles suspended in the air. There can be as many as 500-600 particles in each cubic centimeter, although normally there are fewer than half this number. However, the particles in non-precipitating clouds are normally quite small (averaging about 0.01 mm in radius and rarely exceeding 0.1 mm), and so they fall to earth very slowly. In calm air, a droplet having a radius of 0.05 mm falls at the rate of less than ½ m/sec (1 mph). This maximum fall velocity, known as the *terminal velocity,* is imposed by air resistance. Most clouds are formed when air is rising (as will be seen in Chap. 3), so that in practice, even in extremely weak upward air currents, drops of this size can be suspended in the atmosphere for many hours. In fact, clouds begin to precipitate only when some of the drops within them reach sufficient size to fall through the air with an appreciable velocity.

Cloud types

Aside from observation of the internal makeup of clouds, the outward appearance of clouds is of significance to the meteorologist in interpreting the physical processes in the atmosphere, and is often a harbinger of the weather to come. The basic clouds are identified on the basis of their form and approximate height above the ground where they normally occur. The names of the basic clouds are composed of the following roots: *cirrus,* meaning feathery or fibrous; *stratus* (stratified or in layers); *cumulus* (heaped up); *alto* (middle); and *nimbus* (rain). The ten basic clouds are:

> *High* (base above 7 km, or 23,000 ft, generally composed entirely of ice crystals): *cirrus* (Ci), *cirrostratus* (Cs), *cirrocumulus* (Cc).
>
> *Middle* (2-7 km, or 6,500-23,000 ft): *altocumulus* (Ac), *altostratus* (As).
>
> *Low* (below 2 km, or 6,500 ft): *stratus* (St), *stratocumulus* (Sc), *nimbostratus* (Ns).
>
> *Clouds of vertical development* (base usually below 2 km, or 6,500 ft, but top can extend to great heights): *cumulus,* (Cu), *cumulonimbus* (Cb).

Illustrations of these clouds appear in U.S. Weather Bureau publications, encyclopedias, and many other places and so will not be given here. Some common adjectives applied to the basic names to further describe particular clouds are:

> *Uncinus:* hook-shaped; applied to cirrus, often shaped like a comma.
>
> *Castellanus:* turreted; applied most often to cirrocumulus and altocumulus.
>
> *Lenticularis:* lens-shaped; applied mostly to cirrostratus, altocumulus, and stratocumulus; occurs where air currents are undulating sharply in the vertical, as sometimes occurs on the lee side of mountains.
>
> *Fractus:* broken; applied only to stratus and cumulus.
>
> *Humilis:* lowly; poorly developed in the vertical; applied to cumulus.
>
> *Congestus:* crowded together in heaps, like a cauliflower; applied to cumulus.

As will be shown in Chap. 3, almost all clouds result from the rapid cooling of air when it ascends. In stratiform clouds, the motion in the vertical is generally small, while in cumuliform clouds, the upward and downward velocities are much stronger.

Precipitation

Raindrops are usually between one and several millimeters in diameter. Since the average drop diameter in a nonprecipitating cloud is about 0.02 mm, this means that many cloud drops have increased their volume by a factor of 1,000,000 by the time they fall out of a cloud. Such growth cannot be explained merely by further condensation of water vapor on existing water particles. Small particles must therefore unite to form large particles. How this is accomplished is still not completely settled, but the most probable mechanisms are the following:

(1) *Collision and coalescence of particles.* The drops formed in a cloud are not all of the same size. Due to differences in the rate at which condensation proceeds in different parts of a cloud—sometimes separated by very small distances—the largest drops in the cloud may have diameters several times greater than the smallest. As the air swirls about, the larger drops, because of their greater mass, have more inertia than the smaller ones. These large drops tend, therefore, not to follow exactly the same path as the small ones and, as a result, collide and often coalesce (combine) with the small

ones. Repeated collision and coalescence by a drop may cause it to grow so large that it splinters into several drops, which in turn grow by collision and coalescence, thus producing a "chain reaction" of raindrop growth.

(2) *Growth of ice crystals.* Frequently, especially in the middle latitudes, the uppermost layers of clouds will be composed of ice crystals, while the lower layers contain undercooled (at temperatures below 0°C) liquid drops. Through stirring within the cloud, or because of different fall velocities of the particles, ice crystals and undercooled drops become mixed. At the same temperature, the saturation vapor pressure over a liquid surface is greater than that over an ice surface (see inset of Fig. 1-4), and the ice crystals will therefore grow at the expense of the water drops. This growth mechanism, which is called the *Bergeron process* after the Swedish meteorologist who first suggested it, is believed to be quite important in the *initiation* of precipitation, although further growth most likely involves the collision-coalescence of particles described in the previous paragraph.

The importance of the coexistence of ice crystals and undercooled water drops in the initiation of precipitation forms the basis for many modern cloud-seeding experiments. In a cloud that contains few or no ice crystals, dry ice introduced into the cloud may cool enough drops to their freezing point to produce crystals for later growth by the Bergeron process. Undercooled droplets can also be induced to freeze through injection of certain types of materials, such as silver iodide, apparently because the crystal structure of these materials is very similar to that of ice.

Precipitation types

The only difference between drizzle and rain is the size of the water droplets. The diameter of the former is generally less than 0.5 mm. The principal solid forms of precipitation are:

Snow. Ice crystals that have grown as they traverse the cloud. (See Fig. 1-5 for some of the diverse symmetric forms they develop.)

Freezing rain or drizzle. Rain or drizzle that freezes on impact with the ground or objects.

Sleet. Small ice particles or pellets that originated as rain but froze as they traversed a cold air layer near the ground.

Hail. Small balls or chunks of ice with a diameter of 5-50 mm (0.2-2 in.) or more that fall from cumulonimbus clouds. These destructive stones are formed by the successive accretion of water drops around a small kernel of ice falling through a thick cloud; as each drop is frozen onto the nucleus, it may form a new shell, so that many hailstones acquire an onion-like cross section (Fig. 1-6).

Measurement of precipitation

For practical purposes of water supply, meteorologists are concerned with measuring the amount of water reaching the earth's surface. This is done by sampling the depth of water that would cover the surface if the water did not run off or filter into the soil. A rain gauge is merely a collection pail with a

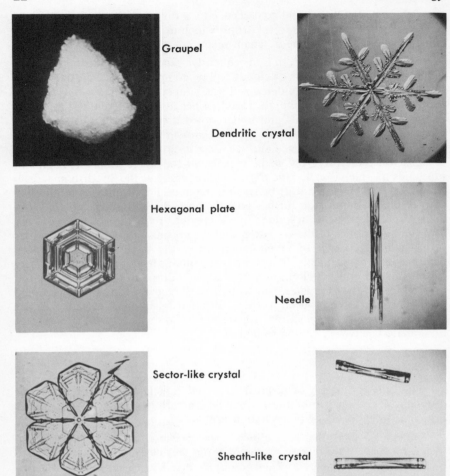

Graupel

Dendritic crystal

Hexagonal plate

Needle

Sector-like crystal

Sheath-like crystal

Fig. 1-5. Some forms of snow crystals. (Courtesy of C. Magono, Hokkaido University, Japan.)

ruler to measure the depth of water. The depth is usually measured in increments of a hundredth of an inch or a millimeter. Solid forms of precipitation are melted and the equivalent liquid depth recorded. In the case of snow, which may remain on the ground for a long period of time and thus serve as a natural water reservoir, the snow depth is of interest. Normally, the ratio of snow depth to liquid equivalent is about 10 to 1, although sometimes it is as much as 30 to 1.

Precipitation amounts are extremely variable from place to place, even during a single storm, so that the problem of adequate sampling over an area is a serious one. In most places of the world, not more than one 8-in. diameter rain gauge is installed in every 100 square miles, which is a ratio

(a)   (b)

Fig. 1-6. (a) Hailstones. (b) Cross section of a hailstone. (Courtesy of R. List, SLF.)

of areas of 25 in.^{2} to $(100 \times 5,280 \times 12)^2$ in.^{2}, or approximately $1:10^{12}$; this is somewhat like taking a single hair from one Californian's head to characterize the hair of everyone in the state. In mountainous areas especially, amounts may vary by a factor of two or three in a distance of less than 10 miles. (Along the northeast slopes of Hawaii, the annual rainfall varies from 15 in. to over 300 in. in a distance of about 15 miles.) Interpretation of measured amounts must be done with considerable care. Even at the same point, annual amounts vary greatly, especially in semi-arid climates; the year-to-year amounts can easily fluctuate by 50 per cent or more of the long-term average annual precipitation. For this reason, claims by rainmakers that they have increased the rainfall by some precise figure, like 10.4 per cent, should be viewed with a great deal of skepticism.

Wind

Air in motion, or *wind*, is the "equalizer" of the earth's atmosphere. By transporting heat, moisture, pollutants, etc., from one place to another, it acts to redistribute the concentration of these quantities. Chapter 3 will discuss what causes winds; at this point, only some of the general characteristics of wind will concern us.

Although air moves up and down as well as horizontally, the speed of vertical displacements is usually a tenth or less of the horizontal component. Even though it is quite small, the vertical component is very important. As we shall see later, it is the up-and-down motion of air particles that is principally responsible for the formation and dissipation of clouds in the atmosphere. Only the *horizontal* component of the wind is measured on a regular basis, while the much smaller vertical component must be computed from relationships between it and the changes of the horizontal wind in space.

Measurement of wind

Many instruments are used to measure the horizontal wind velocity near the surface of the earth. The wind vane is a very old device for indicating wind direction. Because it points *into* the wind, it is customary to designate wind direction as that *from* which the air comes. Thus, when the air is moving *from* northwest (315°) *to* southeast (135°), the wind direction is said to be northwest (315°).

A large variety of *anemometers* exists for measurement of wind speed. The cup anemometer is probably the most widely used. It consists of three or more hemispherical cups clustered around a vertical shaft. Air striking concave sides of the cups exerts more force than that hitting the convex sides, causing the cups and therefore the shaft to turn. The number of rotations per unit time is a measure of the wind speed.

Air flow is retarded by friction with the ground and deflected by obstacles, so that the position of wind-measuring instruments must be carefully considered. At an airport, for example, both the wind speed and direction atop the control tower may be considerably different than at the end of the runway. Typically, the wind speed increases rapidly with height near the surface, so that the height of an anemometer will greatly influence the speed recorded. Unfortunately, there is no uniformity of height for anemometers, although arbitrary standards have been set.

Gustiness and the diurnal wind variation

Anyone who has watched a wind vane oscillate and a cup anemometer alternately increase and decrease its rotation speed during brief periods of time, or who has watched a flag flutter in the wind, can attest to the normal unsteadiness of the wind. An example of such fluctuation can be seen from the recording of the wind direction and speed of Fig. 1-7. These velocity

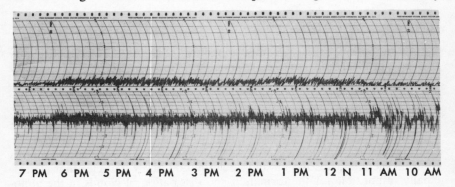

7 PM   6 PM   5 PM   4 PM   3 PM   2 PM   1 PM   12 N   11 AM   10 AM

Fig. 1-7.   Example of a wind's fluctuations during the day.

changes are attributed to the fact that air normally does not move in straight lines, but in tortuous paths. We call such erratic air flow patterns *turbulent*. Successive particles passing a single point in space may have had distinctly different histories, some having been most recently at higher elevations than the point, others at lower elevations. Normally, those coming from higher up will arrive with relatively high velocities, while those coming from lower elevations will have relatively low velocities. The result will be a gusty wind velocity at the observation point.

Turbulent and gusty winds are most pronounced during midday, when the vertical stratification of the air (Chap. 3) is least, and weakest during the night, when the stability of the air tends to suppress vertical displacement of the flow. For the same reason, the winds near the surface tend to be stronger in the afternoon than they are during the night.

Upper-Air Observations

Winds at levels above the reach of ground-based instruments are measured by tracking helium- or hydrogen-filled balloons. The horizontal displacements over short intervals of time as the balloon ascends give the velocity. The changes in position of the balloon may be determined by any of these methods: (1) optically, by the use of a theodolite (similar to a surveyor's transit): (2) by reflection of radio waves (radar) from a target carried by the balloon; (3) by tracking of the radio signal transmitted by a radiosonde carried by the balloon.

Systematic measurements of meteorological conditions in the free atmosphere high above the surface began around the turn of the century. Until 1938, when the radiosonde came into use, the sounding instruments had to be retrieved before the data became available. Instruments recording temperature, humidity, and pressure were carried aloft by balloons, kites, and airplanes. In the case of a free balloon, the instrument drops to the earth on a parachute, and the processing of the data had to wait until some finder returned the instrument. Kites were extremely laborious to handle and they rarely reached heights greater than 3 km. Airplane soundings were expensive, and, at least in the early days, could not provide data to the altitudes desired, or during periods of severe weather.

The radiosonde, carried aloft by balloons, transmits its measurements by radio back to a ground station. The radiosonde used in the United States consists of a lightweight, cheap radio transmitter that emits a continuous signal. The temperature- and humidity-measuring elements control the frequency or amplitude (intensity) of the audio output of the radio signal. An aneroid barometer cell, moving a contact arm across a series of metal strips, alternately connects temperature and humidity into the circuit. By setting consecutive contacts for known pressure intervals, the temperature and humidity are recorded as a function of pressure. The altitude can be computed if the vertical distribution of temperature, humidity, and pressure is known. The radiosonde is now the principal tool of the meteorologist for systematically observing the conditions of the lowest 30 km of the atmosphere. Exploration of higher levels has been accomplished principally by rockets.

Satellites

Observations of most of the earth's atmosphere are entirely inadequate. About 70 per cent of the earth's surface is covered by oceans and a large proportion of the rest is dominated by mountains, snow, deserts, and jungles. Even in populated areas, the density of weather observing stations permits the construction of only a very "coarse-grained" picture of the atmosphere.

The launching of weather satellites promises to improve this situation somewhat. Equipped with television cameras, they transmit to earth pictures of the clouds as seen from above. These photographs have been valuable, especially over the oceans, to pinpoint the locations of storms (Fig. 3-26). On a few occasions, hurricanes (Fig. 3-28) that were undetected by the low-density oceanic network of stations have been uncovered by Tiros weather satellites. Measurements of radiation from the earth also promise to yield increased knowledge of the earth's energy balance (Chap. 2).

A word of caution should be given regarding the extravagant claims sometimes made that satellites have advanced the science of meteorology tremendously. Photographs tell us very little about the complex physical processes going on within the atmosphere, since clouds are merely visual manifestations of the interplay of these processes. Smoke seen from a great distance may indicate that there is a fire, but it does not tell what is burning, or why. The principal value of satellite protographs taken at altitudes of several hundred miles has been in "finding the smoke."

PROBLEMS

1. Compute the average mass of an air molecule from the data given in Fig. 1-1.
2. A light bulb has an air density of about 10^8 molecules/cm^3. At what altitude above sea level is such a vacuum achieved naturally?
3. If you were to construct a scale model of the earth and its atmosphere, starting with a 1-m diameter globe, how far from the surface would the following extend?
   (a) Mt. Everest,
   (b) the level at which 99 per cent of the atmosphere is found,
   (c) the level of the tropopause.
4. Compute the height of a water barometer at a place where the atmosphere's pressure is 850 mb, if the temperature of the barometer is 10°C.
5. Make a list of at least a dozen ways in which the atmosphere—its constituents and its motions—affect man and his activities.
6. As far as "weather" is concerned, which of the atmosphere's gases are most important? What role(s) does each play in the weather-making processes?
7. The average atmospheric density at sea level is about 1.2×10^{-3} gm/cm^3, and the average pressure 1,013 mb. If the density were constant in the vertical, what would be the depth of the atmosphere (at what point would $p = 0$)?

Chapter 2

The Atmosphere's Energy

THE ATMOSPHERE AS A HEAT ENGINE

A convenient way to examine the workings of the atmosphere is through the energy budget. The law of the conservation of energy requires that we account for all of the energy received by the earth, so that by looking at all forms of energy and transformations we have a guide to atmospheric phenomena. This is similar to following in detail what happens to the fuel energy provided in an engine, thereby ending up with a fairly good picture of the operation of the engine. Figure 2-1 presents a schematic energy flow diagram. This and the following chapters will deal with particular portions of the flow diagram.

Practically all of the energy that reaches the earth comes from the *sun*. Intercepted first by the atmosphere, a small part is directly absorbed, particularly by certain gases such as ozone and water vapor. Some of the energy is reflected back to space by the atmosphere, its clouds, and the earth's surface. Some of the sun's radiant energy is absorbed by the earth's surface. Transfers of energy between the earth's surface and the atmosphere occur in a variety of ways, such as radiation, conduction, evaporation, and convection. Kinetic energy (air in motion, or wind) results from differences in temperature within the atmosphere, in much the same way that a heat engine converts differences in heat levels between the inside and outside of the expansion chamber to the motion of the piston. And, finally, friction is constantly bleeding off some of the energy of motion, converting it to heat. The combination of these many processes, which are listed in Fig. 2-1, produces the complex atmospheric phenomena called weather.

SOLAR ENERGY

We start our discussion of atmospheric processes with the sun, the original source of almost all of the earth's energy. The sun is not an unusual star, either in brilliance or in size. A slowly rotating body of hot (several million

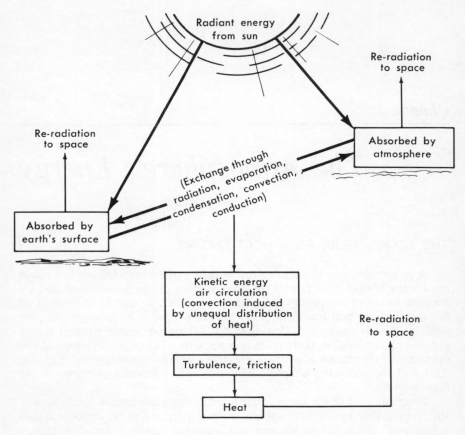

Fig. 2-1. **Energy flow diagram.**

degrees centigrade), very dense gas, with a diameter of about 140,000 km, it is surrounded by a very tenuous atmosphere that extends several solar diameters from the surface. It generates a tremendous amount of heat (about 4×10^{27} cal are radiated every minute), but the earth intercepts less than one part in two billion of this total. Measurements made on the earth indicate that the rate at which energy impinges on a surface perpendicular to the sun's rays at the mean solar-earth distance is about 2.00 cal/cm²/min. This value is known as the *solar constant*, although no one is certain exactly how "constant" is the output of the sun. Variations of the total energy output are probably smaller than the accuracy of the measurements, which is about ±3 per cent. The intermittent outbursts of small particles and very short radiation, associated with disturbances on the sun such as those shown in Fig. 2-2, are largely absorbed in the outermost layers of the atmosphere.

The earth moves in an elliptical path of slight eccentricity around the sun at a mean distance of 149.5×10^6 km. The radiant energy that it receives from the sun covers a broad range of the electromagnetic spectrum, from the very

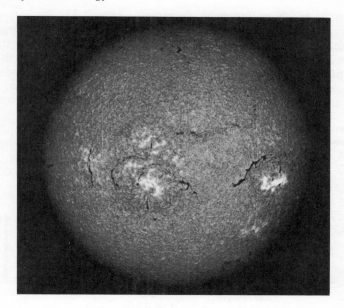

Fig. 2-2(a). The solar disk, as seen in the red wavelength of hydrogen. Dark, thread-like features are "filaments," called "prominences" when seen in profile at the edge of the sun. The bright features are plages, and the dark, rather circular ones in the plage regions are sunspots. (Courtesy of Sacramento Peak Observatory, Sunspot, New Mexico.)

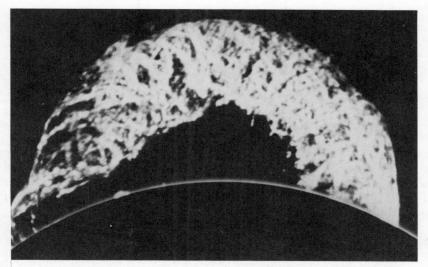

Fig. 2-2(b). Largest solar prominence ever recorded. (June 4, 1946. Courtesy of High Altitude Observatory, Climax, Colorado.) (Sun's face has been blacked out by metal disk in coronagraph used to photograph this phenomenon.)

short gamma and X rays to radio wavelengths (Fig. 2-3). The rate at which energy is emitted from each square centimeter of surface as a function of wavelength is very much like that for an ideal or *black body* at 6,000°K, shown in Fig. 2-4. It can be seen that most of the solar energy falls in the visible portion of the spectrum, with the peak energy occurring at a wavelength of approximately 0.5 micron (0.0005 mm), which is blue-green. (Wavelengths are usually given in microns, abbreviated μ, or in angstrom units,

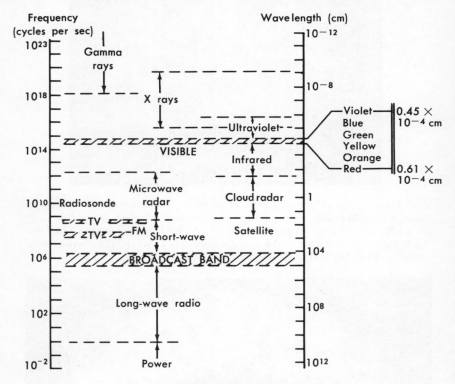

Fig. 2-3. **The electromagnetic spectrum.**

abbreviated Å. One micron is 10^{-4} cm, or 0.0001 cm, and 1 Å $= 10^{-8}$ cm, or 0.00000001 cm.) In contrast, a body at 300°K (27°C, which is a little warmer than the mean temperature of the earth) radiates energy at a rate of 1/160,000 that of a body at 6,000°K, and its maximum emission occurs near 10 μ wavelength, which is the invisible infrared.*

What happens to the enormous amount of energy, in the form of electromagnetic waves, impinging upon the earth? When rays encounter the earth's

---

* Both of these facts are expressed by Planck's radiation law, which states that the rate at which a body radiates energy increases with the fourth power of the absolute temperature ($\propto T^4$) while the wavelength at which it emits most intensely varies inversely with the temperature ($1/T$). Thus, hot bodies not only radiate much more energy than cold bodies, but they do it at shorter wavelengths. "Red hot" is not as hot as "blue hot."

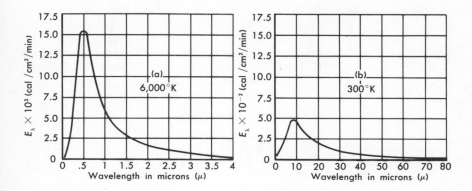

In comparing the two curves, note that the vertical scale of
the 300°K curve is 100,000 times that of the 6000°K curve

**Fig. 2-4. Black body emission of (a) a hot body such as the sun and (b) a
cool body such as the earth.**

atmosphere, some pass through undisturbed, some are absorbed by the atmosphere, and the rest are turned back. We shall examine the ways in which
all three of these occur:

(1) *Absorption.* Oxygen, ozone, water vapor, carbon dioxide, and dust
particles are the most significant absorbers of the "short-wave" radiation from
the hot sun and the "long-wave" radiation of the cool earth. The gases are
selective absorbers, meaning that they absorb strongly in some wavelengths,
weakly in others, and hardly at all in still others. The very short ultraviolet
(less than 0.20 μ) radiation of the sun is absorbed as it encounters and splits
molecular oxygen into two atoms in the upper levels of the atmosphere (Fig.
1-1). Ozone, formed by the combination of O and O_2, effectively absorbs
ultraviolet light of longer wavelengths—those between 0.22 and 0.29 μ. The
top portion of Fig. 2-5 illustrates the relative effectiveness of oxygen and
ozone as absorbers. Absorptivity is the fractional part of incident radiation
that is absorbed. It can be seen that oxygen and ozone absorb almost 100
per cent of all radiation at wavelengths less than 0.29 μ. For this reason, only
a minute portion of the sun's ultraviolet radiation penetrates to the lower
levels of the atmosphere. In the longer wavelengths neither of these gases
absorbs very much energy, except for a narrow band (near 9.6 μ) in the
infrared. About 2 per cent of the sun's total radiation received on earth is
depleted by ozone.

Water vapor is a significant absorber of radiation. Its complicated absorptivity characteristics are illustrated in the lower half of Fig. 2-5. Although
not effective at wavelengths below 0.8 μ, where most of the *solar* radiation
exists, it absorbs strongly between 5 and 7 μ, and moderately well beyond
15μ, wavelengths at which the cool earth and its atmosphere emit much of
their energy (Fig. 2-4).

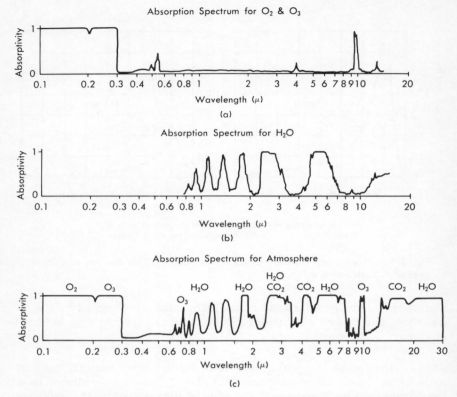

Fig. 2-5. Absorption of radiation at various wavelengths by (a) O_2 and O_3, (b) H_2O, and (c) the principal absorbing gases ($1\mu = 1/1000$ mm).

In summary, the atmosphere is essentially transparent between 0.3 and 0.8 μ, where most of the solar (short-wave) radiation occurs. But between 0.8 and 2 μ, where much of the terrestrial (long-wave) radiation is emitted, there are several bands of moderate absorptivity by water vapor.

(2) *Reflection by clouds.* Most clouds are excellent reflectors, but poor absorbers, of radiant energy. The absorption by clouds depends on their thickness and the size of the drops they contain, but they usually do not absorb more than 10 per cent of the energy incident on them. On the average, about half of the reflected radiation from clouds goes upward and the other half downward toward the earth's surface, although the proportion depends on the type of clouds and the amount of sky covered.

(3) *Scattering.* The atmosphere is composed of many, many discrete particles—gas molecules, dust, water droplets, etc.—but the empty space between particles is actually greater than the volume occupied by the particles. Each particle acts as an obstacle in the path of radiant energy (e.g., light waves) traveling through the atmosphere, much as rocks in a lake impede the progress of ripples in the water. The wave fronts are deformed by

these obstacles into a pattern that makes it appear that the rays emanate from the obstacles. Thus, radiant energy propagating in a single direction is dispersed in all directions as it encounters each particle in its path. This dispersion of the energy is called *scattering*.

The effectiveness of a particle as a scattering center depends on its volume. For particles the size of gas molecules, the amount of scattering is much higher for the short wavelengths of light (blue) than for the long waves (red). It is for this reason that the white light of the sun and the moon becomes yellow or red on the horizon, while the sky, which is lit by scattered light, is blue. Astronauts have observed, as they ascend through the atmosphere, that the sky becomes darker, finally becoming black, as the density of the scattering particles decreases.

When the atmosphere contains many large dust particles or minute water droplets (haze), scattering is no longer very selective in terms of wavelength. The long waves are scattered almost as much as the short waves, and the resulting sky color becomes less bluish and more white or milky. In fact, the blueness of a cloudless sky is an indication of its "purity," i.e., how free it is of smoke, dust, and haze.

On the average, about 12 per cent of the sun's radiation striking the earth's atmosphere is scattered; half of the scattered radiation is lost to space.

Figure 2-6 presents a summary of what happens, on the average, to the solar radiation intercepted by the earth. Although normally about 50 per cent of the earth's surface is covered by clouds, they are generally poor absorbers of short-wave radiation. Approximately 17 per cent is absorbed by the gases and dust of the atmosphere, principally by water vapor. This means that a total of 19 per cent is absorbed as the rays traverse the atmosphere.

The earth's surface absorbs about 47 per cent of the solar radiation: some of it (19 per cent) comes directly from the sun, some (23 per cent) after reflection by clouds, and the rest (5 per cent) after being scattered by the air. The reflectivity of the earth's surface varies greatly, of course. Some fresh snow fields and water surfaces (when the sun is close to the horizon) reflect 90 per cent or more of the incident rays. But a forest may reflect less than 10 per cent and green grass fields only 10-15 per cent.

Thus, of the total energy arriving from the sun (2 cal/cm²/min), approximately 66 per cent is absorbed by the earth's surface and atmosphere. The rest, 34 per cent, is lost to space, having been reflected by clouds and the earth's surface or scattered by the particles in the air. The average reflectivity, "whiteness," or *albedo* of the earth is said, therefore, to be 0.34, since that is the fractional part of the incident radiation that is bounced off the earth. For purposes of comparison, the moon's albedo is only about 7 per cent, which means that it is not nearly as bright as the earth.

THE EARTH'S HEAT BALANCE

Studies indicate that over moderately long periods of time (between hundreds and thousands of years) the mean temperature of the earth is essentially constant. This would indicate that there exists a long-term heat balance

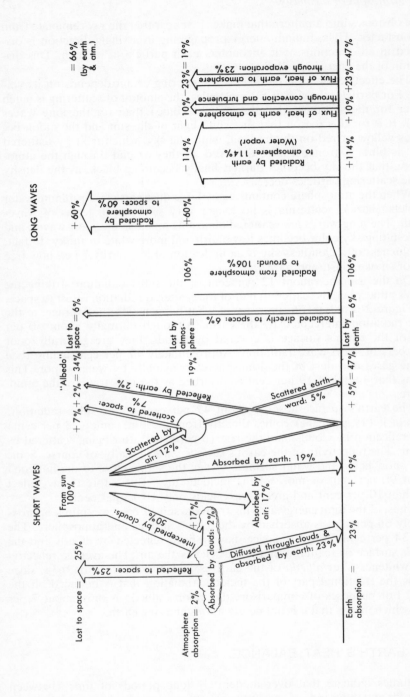

Fig. 2-6. The earth's heat balance.

between the earth and space. It follows, then, that since 66 per cent of the solar energy striking the earth is absorbed, an equal amount must be reradiated to space. Figure 2-6 shows what happens to the earth's energy. Note that 66 per cent is lost by the earth and its atmosphere to space. Keep in mind, though, that although there is a heat balance for the planet as a whole, all parts of the earth and its atmosphere are not in radiative balance. In fact, it is the imbalance between incoming and outgoing energy over the earth that leads to the creation of wind systems that act to alleviate the surpluses and deficits of heat that would otherwise result.

Of special interest in the long-wave energy transfers is the fact that the amounts emitted by the earth and the air actually exceed the total solar energy amount retained by the earth (66 per cent). This can be explained in terms of the "blanketing" effect of the atmosphere, which keeps the earth's surface and lower layers of the atmosphere a good deal warmer than they would be without the atmosphere. For example, the moon's lit surface, which absorbs almost twice as much energy per unit area as does the earth's surface, is more than 20°C colder because it lacks an atmospheric "blanket."

Two gases—water vapor and carbon dioxide—play the most important role in keeping the earth warm. Except for a "window" between about 8.5 and 11 μ (Fig. 2-5), these gases block the direct escape of the infrared energy emitted by the earth's surface. (A "cool" body such as the earth emits most of its energy in the infrared, as shown in Fig. 2-4.) Although the atmosphere is relatively transparent to the short-wave solar radiation (only 19 per cent is absorbed, Fig. 2-6) it is quite opaque to the long-wave terrestrial radiation. Only when the surface temperature is fairly high, is the radiational loss through the transparent bands and from the "top" of the atmosphere sufficient to equal the 66 per cent received in short waves. This heat-retaining behavior of the atmosphere is analogous to what happens in a greenhouse, and for this reason it is referred to as the *greenhouse effect*. The effect is quite noticeable when one compares the nocturnal temperature drop when the air is dry (as over deserts) to that when the air is moist.

DISTRIBUTION OF HEAT ENERGY OVER THE EARTH

As mentioned above, although the overall income and outgo of radiant energy are essentially in balance, they are not in balance everywhere on the earth. This is mostly due to the fact that the amount of incoming energy varies greatly from place to place. It is also caused, to a lesser extent, by variations in the intensity of outgoing radiation. The amount of energy *emitted* by the earth and the atmosphere to space is controlled largely by the amount of moisture in the air; the distribution of solar energy *absorbed* by the earth's surface is controlled mostly by the earth's movements, the distribution of physical properties of the surface, and cloudiness.

The latitudinal variations of absorbed solar energy can be easily understood if one bears in mind three facts: (1) the earth is essentially a sphere, (2) the sun is so far away that its rays of light are approximately parallel, and (3) the earth is rotating. Only one-half of the sphere can be illuminated at one time, and the angle that the sun's rays make with the sphere's surface will decrease from 90° at the exact center of the lit circle to 0° at the edges (where the shadow begins). This is illustrated in the left side of Fig. 2-7. Angle *c* equals 90° at the one point where the sun's rays are perpendicular to the

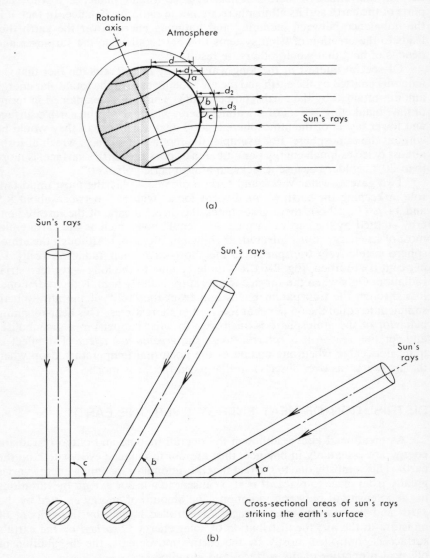

Fig. 2-7. The intensity of solar radiation depends on the angle at which the sun's rays strike the earth's surface: (a) shows the angles of incidence *a, b, c* and the depths of penetration through the atmosphere, d_1, d_2, d_3, at different parallels of latitude; (b) shows the different cross-sectional areas on earth's surface due to different angles of incidence.

surface, while angle *b* is less than 90°, and angle *a* is less than angle *b*. The rays entering with the angle *a* will, of course, traverse a greater mass of atmosphere than those entering with angle *b* or *c* (since distance $d_1 > d_2 > d_3$), and therefore will be subject to greater depletion by absorption, reflection, and scattering. But even more important, the intensity will be less at lower solar angles because the same amount of energy will intercept larger surface areas, as is illustrated in the right half of Fig. 2-7, so that the amount of energy received by each square kilometer of surface will be less for low angles of the sun than for high ones.

Finally, the earth rotates about an axis, so that the half of the sphere being illuminated is continuously changing. Consider the ring formed by the circular edge of the earth's shadow. When the axis of rotation lies in the same plane as this ring, it is evident that the ring will divide each latitude circle exactly in half, so that all places will have precisely 12 hours of sunlight and 12 hours of darkness each day. But when the axis of rotation does not fall in the plane of the shadow's ring, the latitude circles will not be divided into two equal parts, except at the equator. The ratio of night to day at each latitude will be in the same proportion as the two segments of the latitude circle created by the shadow ring.

The axis of rotation sometimes coincides with the "shadow ring" and sometimes does not, as the earth moves in its annual course around the sun. The axis of rotation is not perpendicular to the plane containing the path of the earth's revolution, but rather it is tilted at an angle of 23½° from the normal. This means that only at the equinoxes (March 21 and Sept. 23, approximately) does the axis lie in the plane of the shadow ring.

Figure 2-8 shows the way in which the total energy (*insolation*) received each day varies with time of year and latitude. Note that in the summer, in both hemispheres, the total daily energy received varies little between the poles and the equator; this is because the lower solar angles in the polar regions are compensated for by the greater duration of sunshine each day. In the winter, of course, the latitudinal variation in the amount of energy received is very great, since practically none is received at high latitudes while the equatorial region's supply remains almost unchanged throughout the year.

There is a slight difference between the two hemispheres in the distribution of energy received throughout the year. You will note from Fig. 2-8 that the Southern Hemisphere receives a little more energy in its summer than does the Northern Hemisphere in its summer, and conversely during their respective winters. The small differences are due to the fact that the earth moves in a slightly elliptical path about the sun, and at the beginning of January the sun and the earth are closest together (*perihelion*). The difference in total energy received by the earth between *aphelion* and perihelion is only 7 per cent.

The amount of incoming and outgoing energy, averaged over the entire year, is shown for each latitude in Fig. 2-9. It can be seen that, as would be expected, the incoming short-wave energy decreases a great deal between the equator and the poles, while the outgoing long-wave energy is nearly constant. Although the *total* incoming energy for all latitudes (curve I) equals the

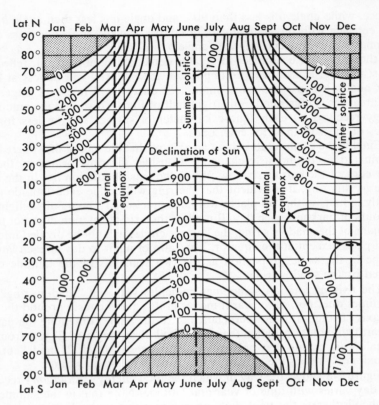

Fig. 2-8. **Undepleted insolation, in cal/cm²/day, as a function of latitude and dates. Cross-hatched areas represent latitudes within the earth's shadow.**

total outgoing energy for all latitudes (curve II), income equals outgo only at a single latitude; there is a surplus of energy income at tropical latitudes and a deficit in the polar regions. If air movements (and, to a lesser extent, ocean currents) did not exist to redistribute the energy, the poles would become steadily colder and the tropics steadily warmer.

If there were only latitudinal variations in the energy received and absorbed by the earth and its atmosphere, meteorology would be a considerably simpler study. However, the absorptive properties of the air and the surface of the earth are not distributed in a smooth, unchanging pattern. The radiation absorption properties of the atmosphere depend on the clouds, moisture, and dust in the air, the concentrations of which may vary both geographically and with time. Surface properties are also erratically distributed over the face of the earth, and even they change with time.

The most pronounced differences in surface thermal properties are those between land and sea. Under identical insolation conditions (same solar angles, duration of daylight, atmospheric transparency), the temperature changes experienced by the water will be much less than those of the land

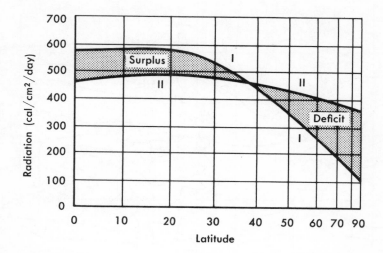

Fig. 2-9. Curves I and II represent mean annual insolation and outgoing long-wave flux, respectively, at the tropopause.

surface. The principal reason for this is that water is a fluid and so can be mixed; as a result, its heat tends to be distributed over a much greater mass than is the case with "stagnant" land. The heat absorbed by a land surface tends to be confined in the upper few inches, while in water, the heat may be distributed to depths of hundreds of feet. There are other reasons for the smaller temperature range of water surfaces: (1) because water is transparent, radiation can penetrate to depths of tens or even hundreds of feet, so that the energy is absorbed by a great mass of water; (2) water generally has a higher specific heat than does land (i.e., more heat is required to raise the temperature of a gram of water 1 °C than for land); and (3) some heat is used in evaporation of water (latent heat).

The fact that the oceans act as heat reservoirs is illustrated by the January and July mean air temperature maps of Fig. 2-10. Note how much more the temperature varies between seasons over middle and high latitudes over the continents than it does over the oceans. For example, at latitude 45°N, the annual range of temperature over the continents is about 60°F, while over the Pacific Ocean at the same latitude, the range is only about 10°F. Note also how the isotherms dip equatorward over the oceans in summer and poleward in the winter, indicating that the ocean is cooler than the land in summer and warmer than the land in winter.

TEMPERATURE LAG

The times of high and low air temperatures do not coincide with the times of maximum and minimum solar radiation, either on an annual or daily

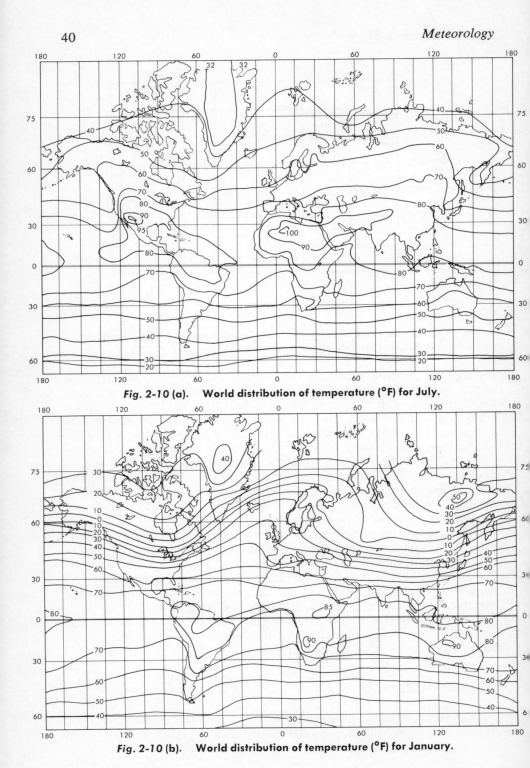

Fig. 2-10 (a). **World distribution of temperature (°F) for July.**

Fig. 2-10 (b). **World distribution of temperature (°F) for January.**

basis. The months of July and August are generally the hottest of the year, January and February the coldest. Yet, on an annual basis, the greatest intensity of radiation occurs in June and the lowest in December and the greatest temperature of the day normally occurs at 3 or 4 P.M., yet the greatest intensity of insolation each day occurs near noon.

This *lag* in the temperature can be explained on the basis of the time required for heating and cooling. (See Fig. 2-11.) The earth loses heat con-

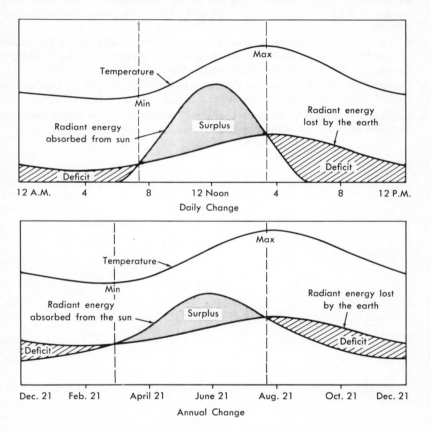

Fig. 2-11. The daily and annual temperature maxima and minima "lag" behind the maxima and minima of solar radiation.

tinuously through radiation, as does any body that has heat energy. During some months of the year and some hours of the day, the incoming energy exceeds the outgoing energy of the earth. When this is occurring, the temperature will be increasing, since the air's heat content will be rising. The maximum temperature will occur at the time when the incoming energy ceases to exceed the outgoing. Thereafter, when the outgoing energy is greater than the incoming, the temperature will fall until the two are again in balance. At the point in time where a "surplus" of energy begins to appear, the lowest temperature will have occurred.

PROBLEMS

1. Compute the total energy per minute intercepted by the earth and the fraction of the total solar energy output this represents. (Hint: The cross-sectional area of the earth $= \pi r^2 = 3.1416 \times (6,000)^2$ km^2, while the surface area of an imaginary sphere surrounding the sun at the distance of the earth from the sun $= 4\pi d^2 = 4 \times 3.1416 \times (140,000)^2$ km^2. The solar constant $= 2.00$ cal/cm^2/min)

2. If you were attempting to observe the temperature distribution on the moon's surface by measuring the infrared radiation, what wavelength band would give the best results, considering the atmosphere's transparency?

3. Compute the elevation angle of the sun at noon at the latitude of your city on Oct. 21. What will be the length of the daylight (not counting twilight)?

4. Explain why nighttime temperatures are generally lower on nights when the humidity is low than when it is high.

Chapter 3

Air in Motion

The uneven distribution of heat resulting from latitudinal variations of insolation and from differences in absorptivity of the earth's surface leads to air motions. The mechanics of this conversion of heat energy to kinetic energy will be the subject of this chapter.

We will be examining the deviations of air motion from those that are due to the planetary motion. The atmosphere as a whole follows the earth in its movements through space; it also rotates with the earth from west to east, so that at the equator the air moves eastward at a speed of more than 1,000 mph, while at latitude 60° it moves eastward at half that speed, and, of course, at the poles its eastward speed is zero. Because the ground moves at the same eastward speed, these motions go unnoticed by the earthbound observer. Winds are those motions of the air *relative* to the earth.

PRINCIPAL FORCES IN THE ATMOSPHERE

According to *Newton's first law,* for a body to change its state of motion, it must be acted upon by an unbalanced force. There are two classes of forces that affect the atmosphere: (1) those that exist regardless of the state of motion of the air and (2) those that arise *only after* there is motion. The first category can be thought of as the fundamental or basic forces, since without them there would be no motion. These basic "driving" forces are produced by gravitational attraction and pressure. Among the second group of forces are friction or "drag," centripetal, and Coriolis forces.

The "Driving" Forces

The gravitational pull of the earth is always directed downward; the strength with which it acts on any "parcel" of fluid is proportional to the mass of the parcel. The only way a parcel of fluid can experience a net force due to pressure in some particular direction is if one "side" of the parcel is being acted on by a pressure different from that acting on the opposite "side." In Fig. 3-1, the fluid in the pipe will remain stationary if the pressure $p_1 (= F_1/A)$

43

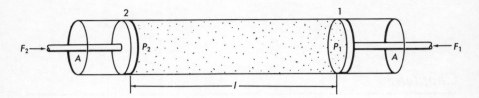

Fig. 3-1. Pressure gradient in a pipe. (A = cross-sectional area of pipe; l = distance between pistons.)

at the face of the piston on the right is equal to the pressure p_2 ($= F_2/A$) at the piston face on the left. Only if the two forces, F_1 and F_2 (or the two pressures, p_1 and p_2), *differ* will the fluid accelerate. According to *Newton's second law,* the magnitude of the *acceleration* experienced will then depend on the net force ($F_1 - F_2$) and on the mass being acted upon.

Assuming that the pipe has a cross-sectional area A, the volume of the mass of fluid on which the net force $F_1 - F_2$ is acting is given by $A \times l$, where l is the distance between the pistons. Therefore, the net force acting on each unit volume of fluid is

$$\frac{F_1 - F_2}{A \times l} = \frac{p_1 - p_2}{l}$$

Thus, the force per unit volume in a fluid is directly proportional to the pressure difference, and inversely proportional to the distance. This ratio of pressure increment to distance, $(p_1 - p_2)/l$, is called the *pressure gradient,* since it measures the grade or slope of the pressure. The direction of the acceleration will be "down slope," i.e., from high to low pressure. In Fig. 3-1, if $p_1 > p_2$ the acceleration will be from right to left.

Of the two principal forces producing accelerations in the atmosphere— gravity and pressure gradient—the first *always* acts vertically downward, but the second can theoretically act in any direction. However, in the atmosphere the pressure gradient is almost entirely directed in the vertical also. Figure 3-2 illustrates a typical pressure pattern in a vertical cut of the atmosphere. The slope shown has been greatly exaggerated, since typical distances for b and c would be 40 m and 200 km, respectively (a slope of only 40:200,000, or a 1-km height change in 500 km). Thus, the *horizontal* pressure gradient in this example would be 4 mb/200 km = 1 mb/50 km = 0.2×10^{-4} mb/m, while the *vertical* pressure gradient would be 4 mb/50 m = 1 mb/10 m = 0.1 mb/m; the pressure gradient force in the *vertical* is thus almost 10,000 times that in the *horizontal*. Because the vertical portion of the pressure gradient is so much greater than the horizontal, and since gravity acts *only* in the vertical, it is customary to treat horizontal forces (and motions) separately from those in the vertical.

In the vertical, the pressure always decreases with height (since the mass of fluid remaining above must decrease with height), so the acceleration acting on a parcel by the pressure gradient must always be directed upward.

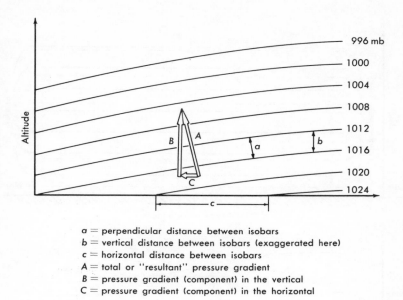

a = perpendicular distance between isobars
b = vertical distance between isobars (exaggerated here)
c = horizontal distance between isobars
A = total or "resultant" pressure gradient
B = pressure gradient (component) in the vertical
C = pressure gradient (component) in the horizontal

Fig. 3-2. **Distribution of isobaric surfaces in a vertical cross section. (Note that the slope of the isobars has been greatly exaggerated in this figure. The distance c is much greater than the distance b.)**

The gravitational pull on a parcel is, of course, always downward. It is the net difference between these oppositely directed forces that determines whether a parcel will accelerate upward or downward and at what rate. Now, what determines the magnitude of the vertical pressure gradient? Since pressure measures the weight per unit area, the change in pressure experienced in, say, a 1,000-ft ascent, will depend on the density of the 1,000-ft column of air of unit area. If the air in the layer is very dense, the pressure drop will be greater than if the air is not so dense. At any particular pressure, the density depends on the temperature (Charles' law); warm air is less dense than cold air. (It also depends slightly on the constituents of the air. Moist air, which is a mixture of air and water vapor, is less dense than dry air because water has a lower molecular weight—18—than the average for dry air —29.) Therefore, the vertical pressure gradient will be greater in *cold* air columns than in *warm* ones.

Thermal Circulation

Consider the north-south cross sections of the atmosphere illustrated in Fig. 3-3. If the temperature does not vary in the horizontal at any level (part a of the figure), the density at any height will be equal everywhere so that the equal-pressure surfaces (*isobars*) and equal-density surfaces will be straight and horizontal. But if the air to the south is warmer than that in the north

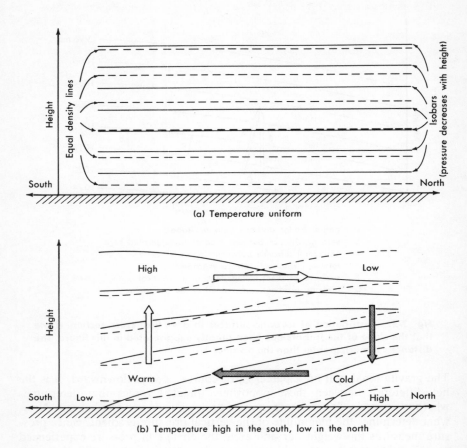

(a) Temperature uniform

(b) Temperature high in the south, low in the north

Fig. 3-3. **The principle of thermal circulation.**

(Fig. 3-3), the density at any level will increase from south to north. The less dense, warm air in the south will rise while the denser, cold air in the north sinks. Near the surface, the pressure surfaces will slope upward toward the colder, denser air of the north. However, because the pressure decreases more rapidly with height in the cold air than it does in the warm, the north-south slope of the isobars will decrease until finally the slope will be reversed. Therefore, although the horizontal flow is always from high to low pressure, near the surface this means north to south (cold to warm) motion, while aloft, it will be just the opposite. The closed circuit formed by the moving parcels of air is a *thermal circulation*. Note that it looks very much like the pattern of motion that occurs in a pan of water that is being heated at one point.

    In summary, there are two rather large "basic" forces acting on the atmosphere: pressure gradient and gravity. The latter is directed entirely in the vertical, while the former has a very small component directed in the horizontal. Even though each of the two forces acting in the *vertical* is much greater than that in the *horizontal,* this does not mean that vertical motion is much stronger than horizontal motion; remember that it is *net* or unbalanced force that determines accelerations, and the two vertical forces are almost always very nearly equal and oppositely directed. Actually, except in small circulation cells such as that of a thunderstorm, the vertical air velocity is normally only a tenth or a hundredth of the horizontal velocity.

FORCES THAT ARISE AFTER THERE IS MOTION

The Effect of the Earth's Rotation

Large-scale flow in the earth's atmosphere does not follow the simple pattern of the thermal circulation shown in Fig. 3-3. The horizontal wind blows more nearly *perpendicular* to the pressure gradient rather than along it. Figure 3-4 shows surface weather maps for the Northern and Southern

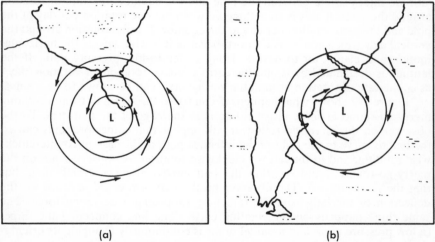

(a)   (b)

Fig. 3-4.   Pattern of wind around an area of low pressure: (a) in the Northern Hemisphere and (b) in the Southern Hemisphere.

hemispheres, with arrows designating the observed wind directions; note that the air is moving more or less *along* the isobars, rather than across them. Evidently something steers the air flow to the right of its target (low pressure) in the Northern Hemisphere and to the left in the Southern Hemisphere. The only thing that could reverse its effect between the two hemispheres is the earth's rotation. This is illustrated by the turntable of Fig. 3-5. The top of the turntable has been given the same sense of rotation (counterclockwise) as the earth's Northern Hemisphere; however, if one looks at the same turntable from below, the sense of rotation is opposite (clockwise).

Imagine yourself on a very large merry-go-round whose rate and sense

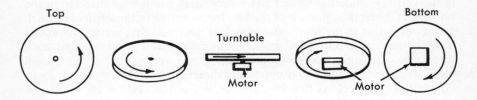

Fig. 3-5.   **Sense of rotation of a turntable as seen from above and below.**

of rotation can be varied. This is the situation of an earthbound observer (Fig. 3-6). At the north pole, an observer is spinning through the vertical axis at a rate of one rotation per day in a counterclockwise sense. At the south pole, an observer is also spinning through the vertical axis at the rate of one rotation per day, but in the opposite (clockwise) sense. At the equator, the observer is not spinning at all around his vertical axis, although his "merry-go-round" is turning about the north-south diameter. At some latitude intermediate between the pole and the equator, the rate of rotation around the vertical axis is something between the one rotation per day at the pole and the zero rotation per day at the equator. It is the rotation around the vertical axis which concerns us most, because it is what affects the horizontal motion and causes air to deviate from a high-to-low pressure path. If the latitude is designated by ϕ and the earth's rate of rotation (1 rotation/day) as ω, the rate of rotation around the vertical axis can be shown to be $\omega \sin \phi$.

Figure 3-7 shows what happens if you try to throw a ball from a rotating merry-go-round at some target riding near the edge of the platform. To the observer on the merry-go-round, it will appear that some force has caused the ball to curve to the right of the intended path in the case of counterclockwise rotation, and to the left for clockwise rotation. An observer not on the merry-go-round would say that the ball moved along a straight line, but that the target turned. The observer on the platform could account for the deflection of the ball from the target by supposing a deviating force. The same thing happens on the rotating earth: The line connecting the target (a low pressure area) and a parcel of air is continuously changing its orientation.

The fictitious deviating force (fictitious *only* as far as a non-rotating observer is concerned) introduced to account for the effect of earth rotation is known as the *Coriolis force,* named for the French mathematician who first explained it mathematically. The algebraic expression for the apparent acceleration is

$$a = 2V\omega \sin \phi$$

where V is the speed of the particle relative to the earth's surface. The magnitude of the acceleration is thus not only dependent on the latitude (maximum at the poles, zero at the equator), but also directly proportional to the speed of the particle. It always acts at a 90° angle to the wind.

Although the Coriolis force is small, it is significant in horizontal air flow

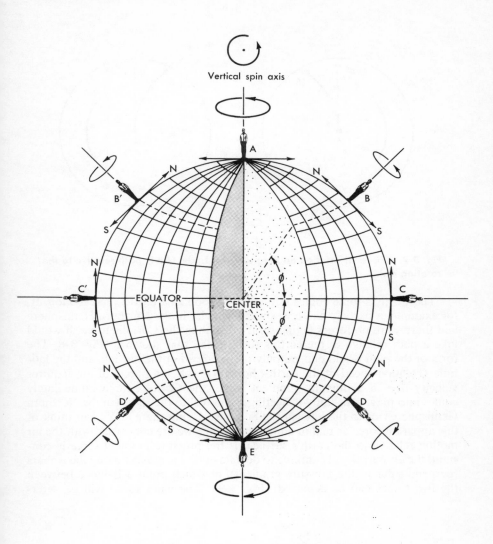

Fig. 3-6. **Horizon rotation rate as a function of latitude.**

because, first of all, the horizontal pressure gradient force is also relatively feeble and, second, the air traverses great distances. It is very important in the large-scale flow, such as that associated with systems that affect the weather over thousands of miles, but it is of much lesser consequence in purely local, small-scale winds. The same, of course, is true in its effect on any body moving freely over the earth's surface. The correction must be applied to long-range artillery, but it has no detectable effect on the path of a bullet. Ocean currents are appreciably affected.

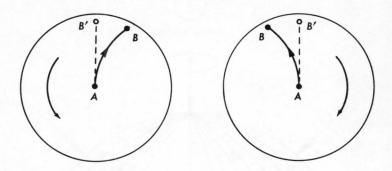

Fig. 3-7. Effect of rotation on the path of a body. (AB is path *relative* to the rotating disk.)

The Coriolis force comes into effect as soon as a particle has motion. If, for example, a particle had a westward velocity in the Northern Hemisphere and there were no forces acting on it other than the Coriolis force, it would take a path relative to the earth's surface like that shown in Fig. 3-8. The form of the path would depend only on the speed of the particle and the latitude (rotation speed of the earth's horizon). When a parcel of air acquires velocity due to a pressure gradient force, the Coriolis force immediately comes into play, constantly deflecting the parcel to the right (in the Northern Hemisphere) or to the left (in the Southern Hemisphere). We can think of this apparent force as real in all respects, since we are concerned with the air motion relative to the earth's surface. If the pressure gradient force is constant, the air parcel will continue to deviate until it is moving along the isobars (perpendicular to the pressure gradient), at which point a balance between the two forces can be achieved (Fig. 3-9). The wind speed will be deter-

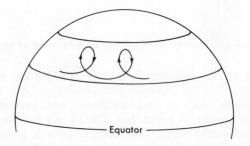

Fig. 3-8. Path of an unaccelerated moving particle relative to the earth's surface.

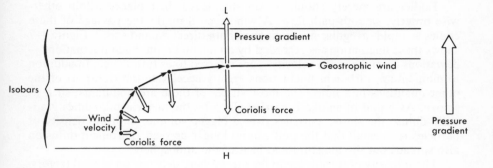

Fig. 3-9. **Approach to geostrophic equilibrium by a parcel of air (N. hemisphere).**

mined by the balance between the Coriolis force and the pressure gradient force, since the magnitude of the former depends on the speed. The flow that results from such a balance is called *geostrophic*.

Friction

Everyone is familiar with the fact that if a wooden box is given a push along a level floor, it will travel a short distance and then stop. The force that retards the forward motion is friction. It is due to the interlocking of surface irregularities and the adhesion of touching molecules of the two contacting surfaces.

Although the adhesion is much less and the space between molecules much greater in a gas, there is, nevertheless, a frictional drag created when velocity differences arise within a gas. This retardation of motion in a fluid is referred to as *viscosity*. When only the random, thermal motion of the *molecules* is responsible for this slowing up, the retardation, sometimes called *molecular viscosity,* is quite low. The effect that the molecular agitation has can be explained as follows: If a stream of air is directed along a smooth, solid surface, the air molecules in contact with the surface will have no motion (other than the usual random agitation), because they adhere to the surface. These "surface" molecules will, in turn, retard the flow of those molecules adjacent to them, because there is a continuous exchange of zero-velocity "surface" molecules with those in the next tier. Some of the slow-moving molecules of the second tier mix with those of the third tier, and so on, causing a progressively lesser retardation with distance from the surface.

The molecular viscosity of air is so small that if it alone were responsible for frictional drag in the atmosphere, the slowing up of the air flow would almost completely disappear within a meter of the surface. Far more significant is the so-called *eddy viscosity* which, at least in the lower layers of the atmosphere, is about 10,000 times more effective than molecular viscosity.

As the name implies, it acts through the transfer of momentum between layers of air by *eddies* rather than by molecules.

Eddies are merely chunks of air that leave their places within otherwise orderly, smooth-path flow. A wind record marks the passage of these eddies as rapid, irregular fluctuations in both direction and speed. Figure 1-7 shows these fluctuations as recorded by an anemograph. Such fluctuations— deviations from the mean velocity—are referred to as turbulence. In addition to momentum, turbulent fluctuations greatly accelerate the transport of the other quantities in a fluid. The most visible of these are pollutants, such as smoke. As a puff of smoke is carried along by the mean wind, eddies gradually diffuse the smoke particles over a bigger volume, until the density of particles is so small that the puff can no longer be seen. Turbulent diffusion also spreads out the moisture and heat of the atmosphere.

The intensity of turbulence in the atmosphere depends on several factors, but the most important are the stability of the atmosphere—how well the atmosphere arrests vertical displacements of air parcels (see Vertical Stability, p. 58), the roughness of the ground, and the speed of the wind. Figure 3-10 illustrates types of behavior of a smoke plume under three different sets of atmospheric conditions.

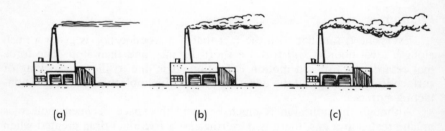

(a)   (b)   (c)

Fig. 3-10. Effect of turbulence in diffusing smoke: (a) laminar (non-turbulent) flow; (b) partially turbulent flow; (c) well-developed turbulence.

The effect of turbulence on the wind is to cause a transfer of momentum through a much deeper layer of air than would occur if only molecular diffusion processes were operating. Depending on the speed of the air flow, the roughness of the underlying surface, and the stability of the atmosphere, the drag of the surface on the flow can extend from anywhere between 300- and 2,000-m elevation. On a day when the atmosphere is well-mixed (curve A in Fig. 3-11a) the surface can be "felt" as high as 2,000 m. In contrast, when the atmosphere is stratified and vertical mixing is suppressed (curve B in Fig. 3-11a) the surface drag extends upward to only 300 m or less. The speed of the wind at the anemometer level (usually 5-10 m above the surface) is only a fraction of the speed in the free atmosphere.

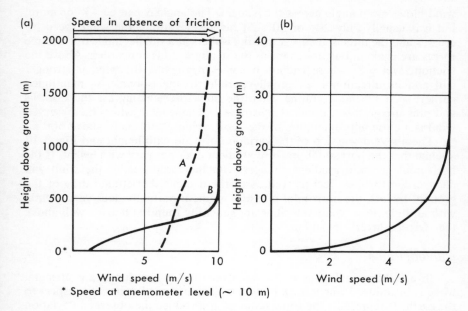

Fig. 3-11. Examples of the variation of wind speed with height in the surface "friction layer": (a) *A* = strong vertical mixing; *B* = weak vertical mixing; (b) variation of wind speed in the first forty meters.

The effect of friction on the horizontal wind that is observed near the ground is illustrated in Fig. 3-12. Near the surface, the frictional drag (always opposed to the direction of air motion) slows up the wind; the Coriolis force is correspondingly less and the "steady" or mean wind is that resulting from a balance of three forces: pressure gradient, Coriolis, and friction. Since the Coriolis force and friction are always at 90° and 180° from the wind direction, respectively, a balance of the three forces can only be achieved if the

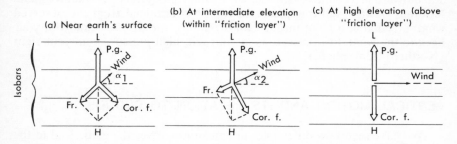

Fig. 3-12. Wind velocity variation in "friction layer" (Northern Hemisphere, constant pressure-gradient). (Cor. f.: Coriolis force; Fr.: friction force; P.g.: pressure gradient force; dashed arrow: resultant of Coriolis and friction forces; α: angle between wind direction and isobars.)

wind blows at an angle across the isobars. The angle α can be 45° or more, but it is usually only 20° or 30°. At higher elevations, the wind speed increases and the direction cuts across the isobars at a smaller angle α; the three forces are again in balance as far as the steady wind is concerned. Above the friction level, i.e., where friction becomes negligible, the wind is stronger still and its direction is essentially parallel to the isobars. As mentioned earlier, such a wind, resulting when the only forces acting are the Coriolis and pressure gradient, is called *geostrophic*. The level at which the observed wind is a close approximation of the geostrophic, is normally above 300 m.

The above discussion of the variation of wind with height and Fig. 3-12 assume that the horizontal pressure gradient does not vary with height. If the horizontal pressure gradient changes with increased height, the wind will change due to this effect as well as to the decreased frictional drag of the ground. In fact, the horizontal pressure gradient normally does vary greatly with altitude. Peak wind velocities are generally found at heights well above the "friction layer": 5-10 km.

Curved Paths

In a fashion analogous to the need for the Coriolis force, a centripetal force is introduced whenever a body moves in a curved path with respect to the earth. It represents the force required to produce the observed deviation of the curved path from a straight line.

When isobars are curved or circular, as they most often are, this additional force comes into play when considering the wind velocity. It always acts along the radius of curvature of the particle's path. The tighter the curve, i.e., the smaller the radius of curvature, the greater is the centripetal force required. The types of flow patterns associated with low pressure areas (*cyclones*) and high pressure areas (*anticyclones*) near the earth's surface in both the Northern and Southern hemispheres are shown in Fig. 3-13. In the Northern Hemisphere, the air is seen to spiral in a counterclockwise sense into a cyclone, and to spiral in a clockwise sense out of an anticyclone. In the Southern Hemisphere the spiral is inward in a clockwise sense for a cyclone, and outward in a counterclockwise sense for an anticyclone. The approximate locations of high and low pressures can be determined from the observed wind direction at a point through *Buys Ballot's rule:* If you stand with your back to the wind, low pressure is to your left, high pressure is to your right (Northern Hemisphere).

VERTICAL MOTION AND ITS RELATION TO CLOUDS

We have seen how differences in temperature over the globe lead to the creation of thermal circulations, associated with vertical and horizontal motions. Because of the important role played by vertical motion in producing weather, some further discussion of how vertical motion is produced and how it affects the formation and dissipation of clouds will be given here.

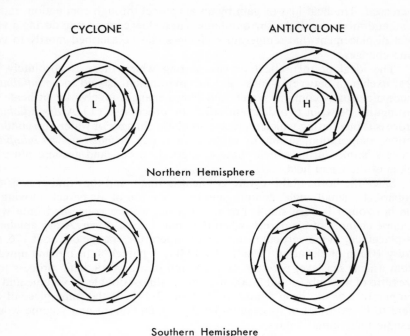

Fig. 3-13.   Cyclonic and anticyclonic flow near the earth's surface.

In discussing the characteristics of the troposphere (Chap. 1), it was mentioned that convection keeps this lowest layer fairly well stirred, in contrast to the stratosphere, in which there is not very much mixing. Yet, on the average, the temperature in the troposphere is not uniform in the vertical, but rather it decreases at the average rate of 6½ °C/km. Evidently, a well-mixed layer of air does not imply one of constant temperature, at least not in the vertical. The reason for this is linked to the pressure changes that air parcels experience during displacements.

Adiabatic Processes

Air displaced vertically experiences especially rapid pressure changes; in response to these changes, the volume must increase or decrease. For example, if a parcel of air is forced to descend at the rate of 1 mile per hour from an elevation of 1 mile, the pressure exerted on it will have increased by about 30 per cent after one hour. If the pressure in a tire is rapidly increased it will heat up; the work done in compression is converted to heat. The heat very slowly dissipates by conduction through the walls of the tire. The same sort of thing occurs when the pressure of an atmospheric air parcel is rapidly increased. The heat loss or gain by an air parcel through conduction, radiation, and mixing with the surroundings is at a slow enough rate during a vertical displacement that temperature changes can be ascribed mostly to volume changes.

The ideal or theoretical process during which there is absolutely no heat exchange between a mass and its environment is said to be *adiabatic*. Since air usually contains water, and phase changes involve latent heat, we distinguish between two different adiabatic processes: (1) A *dry adiabatic* process is one during which there are no phase changes of water (no condensation, evaporation, fusion, or sublimation). (2) A *moist or wet adiabatic* process is one during which phase changes *do* occur, and account must be taken of the latent heat.

Since the horizontal pressure gradient is small, and the wind crosses the isobars at a small angle, compression or expansion of air parcels moving in the horizontal is very small. For this reason, we are concerned only with volume changes of air parcels when they move up or down. A dry abiabatic displacement in the vertical results in a temperature change of about 1°C for every 100 m of elevation (5½ °F/1,000 ft). A parcel of air moving upward from a near sea level pressure of 1,000 mb in a dry adiabatic process to a pressure of 400 mb (about 7,000 m) would almost double its volume and its temperature would drop almost 70°C (Fig. 3-14). If the same piece of air were to be returned to its original level, its temperature and volume would assume their initial values.

During a moist adiabatic process, the changes of phase of the water contained within a parcel of air experiencing a rapid pressure change cause conversion of latent heat to sensible heat, and vice versa. In other words, when condensation is occurring, the latent heat released raises the temperature of the air parcel, and when evaporation is occurring, the latent heat required cools the air. In the example shown in Fig. 3-14, if the air parcel at the 1,000-mb initial pressure is saturated with water vapor (for this to be the case, each kilogram of dry air would have to contain about 12.8 g of water vapor), any lifting of the parcel will cause expansion and cooling, and the excess moisture will have to condense. Thus, when the parcel reaches a pressure of 800 mb (about 2,000 m), the air will still be saturated with water vapor mass, but this saturated vapor mass will be a little more than half the original value. More than 6 g of water in each kilogram of air will have condensed, releasing about $6 \times 600 = 3,600$ cal of latent heat. As a result, the temperature of the air parcel will be considerably (9°C) warmer than it would have been had the process been dry adiabatic. Further ascent of the parcel will cause more condensation, but because the rate at which condensation proceeds is less when the temperature is low than when it is high, the rate of temperature change during a moist adiabatic process is not a constant. (In Fig. 3-14, this can be seen by comparing the temperature change* between 800 and 600 mb—about 12°C over a distance of 2,000 m—with that between 600

---

* The temperature change computed in Fig. 3-14 assumes that only condensation occurs in the air. As mentioned on p. 19, the temperature at which ice particles form in clouds is not fixed. But at the very low temperatures at which they do form, the error introduced by neglect of the heat of fusion is small.

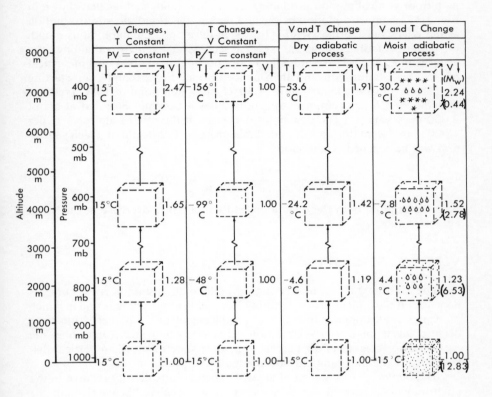

Fig. 3-14. **Change in temperature and volume of an air parcel displaced vertically. Only (c) and (d) assume that there is no heat exchange with the environment. (*T* = temperature; *V* = volume; *P* = pressure; M_w = saturation mass of water vapor mixed with each kilogram of dry air.)**

mb and 400 mb—about 22°C over a distance of about 3,000 m.) About 0.5°C per 100 m is a rough average for the moist adiabatic rate of temperature change.

If the "moist" air parcel illustrated in Fig. 3-14 were to descend, it would warm at the same rate that it cooled during the ascent, *if* all of the liquid and solid particles remained in the parcel. In practice, some of the water drops and ice crystals leave the parcel of air, so that if the parcel later descends, there will be less evaporation and hence a more rapid warming than occurs in the true moist adiabatic process. When some of the condensation products drop out, the process is said to be pseudo-adiabatic, because it is "irreversible."

Condensation in the atmosphere is produced principally through the cooling of air as it ascends, comes under lower pressure, and expands. Similarly, the dissipation of clouds is usually a sign of descending air. The overall pattern of vertical motion producing a cumulus cloud, such as that shown in Fig. 3-17, is upward motion below and within the cloud, downward motion at the edges outside the cloud. (In a well-developed cumulonimbus cloud, the pattern is more complex, as we shall see later.) Even air containing little water vapor (low relative humidity) does not require a great deal of vertical lift to create saturation and then condensation. For example, air starting near sea level with a temperature of 30°C and a dew point of 14°C (relative humidity = 36 per cent, see Appendix 2) will become saturated at about 2,000 m elevation. (The dew point decreases at the rate of almost 2°C per 1,000 m of ascent during a dry adiabatic process. The height at which saturation will be reached is, therefore,

$$\frac{(30° - 14°)}{1°/100 \text{ m} - 0.2°/100 \text{ m}} = 2,000 \text{ m}.$$

After saturation, both the dew point and temperature decrease at the moist adiabatic rate.)

VERTICAL STABILITY

The ability of the atmosphere to produce and sustain vertical currents depends on the atmosphere's "stability." A *stable* atmosphere is one in which buoyancy forces oppose the vertical displacement of air parcels from their original levels; an *unstable* condition exists when buoyancy forces abet the vertical displacement of air parcels; a *neutral* state exists when vertical displacement is neither opposed nor abetted by buoyancy forces.

The buoyancy of a parcel of air will depend on its density relative to the environment density at the same level. If a parcel is "heavier" than the medium surrounding it at the same level, it will be forced to sink; if it is lighter, it will be forced to rise; if its density is the same as that of its surroundings, there will be no "Archimedean force" tending to make it either rise or fall.

Since we do not normally measure density directly in the atmosphere, it is more convenient to discuss stability in terms of temperature, rather than density. From Charles' law (p. 10), we know that at any fixed pressure the density is inversely proportional to the temperature. Therefore, at any given pressure level, we can substitute temperature for density in the statements on buoyancy in the previous paragraph: A parcel of air that is warmer than its surroundings will tend to be pushed upward; one that is colder than its surroundings, downward; and one at the same temperature as its environment will not experience a "push" in either direction.

We have seen from the discussion of adiabatic processes that the temperature of an air parcel displaced vertically changes at a *fixed* rate— 1°C/100 m if there is no water phase transition, and at some lesser rate if there is condensation or evaporation. Evidently, then, whether a vertically displaced parcel of air is warmer or colder than its environment at any particular point along its path will depend on the vertical distribution of ambient atmospheric temperature. The rate at which the temperature decreases vertically in the atmosphere is called the *lapse rate*. (For example, the *average* lapse rate in the troposphere is 6½ °C/km.)

An atmospheric layer in which the lapse rate is less than the adiabatic is stable. This is demonstrated by Fig. 3-15. If a parcel of air at 400 m is displaced upward for some reason, it will always be colder than the environment at the same level; buoyancy will be acting to force the parcel back down. Or, if the same parcel is displaced downward, it will always be warmer than the environment, so that buoyancy will force it back up. In other words, this is a *stable* temperature lapse rate because vertical motions are suppressed. In

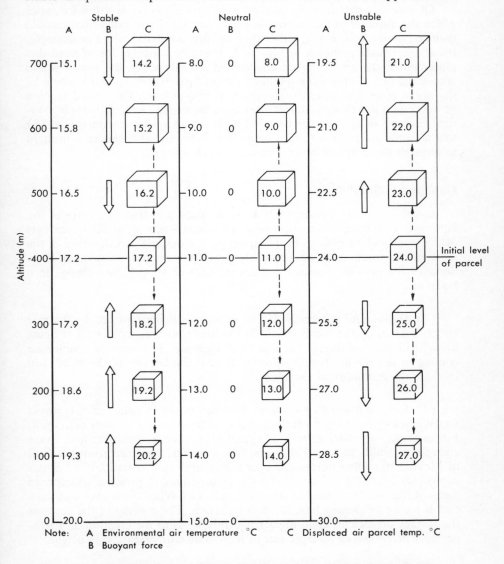

Note: A Environmental air temperature °C   C Displaced air parcel temp. °C
          B Buoyant force

Fig. 3-15. **Stability as a function of lapse rate for dry adiabatic processes.**

the *unstable* case, a parcel displaced upward will be warmer than the environment at each level and, if displaced below the reference level, colder than the environment. Thus, the lapse rate is such that vertical motions are abetted. In the *neutral* case, the lapse rate is exactly equal to the dry adiabatic rate, and therefore the temperature of the parcel at any new level is equal to that of the surrounding air. The criterion, then, for stability in the case of *dry adiabatic* processes is that the lapse rate in the atmosphere layer be less than 1°C/100 m; for instability, greater than 1°C/100 m; and for a neutral state, equal to 1°C/100 m.

Of course, ascending air currents very quickly become saturated, after which the air cools at the *moist adiabatic* rate. The lapse rate criteria would then be based on the moist, rather than the dry, adiabatic rate. For example, the stable situation shown in Fig. 3-15 would be *unstable* for upward displacement if the air parcel were saturated. In ascending, the parcel would cool at the rate of only a few tenths of a degree per 100 m, so that it would be slightly *warmer* than its environment at the 600-m level. Thus, condensation of water with its release of latent heat is an important factor in inducing vertical currents of air. We see here the basis for an earlier statement (p. 15) that a significant portion of the energy that drives the atmosphere is brought in through the evaporation-condensation cycle of water.

Changes in Stability

Lapse rates vary considerably both in space and time. Increase of the lapse rate in a layer of atmosphere results from warming of the lower part of the layer and/or cooling of the upper part. Conversely, a decrease of the lapse rate is produced by cooling of the lower portion and/or warming aloft. Some of the possible causes for different rates of temperature change in a layer are:

(1) *Differential advection.* If the air aloft is being replaced by warmer air brought in by the winds, while in the lower portions colder air is being brought in, the stability of the layer will increase. The opposite, cooler air coming in at high levels and warmer air near the bottom of the layer, will increase the instability of the layer.

(2) *Surface heating or cooling.* This can occur in either of two ways: (a) When air moves over a surface that is either colder or warmer than itself. For example, air moving from an ocean over a warm continent may cause enough instability to set off showers. In the winter, warm air from the Gulf of Mexico streaming northward over the central and eastern United States sometimes is cooled sufficiently by the cold surface to produce widespread areas of fog and low layers of stratus clouds. (b) When air is over a surface that is losing or gaining heat through radiation. The cooling of the air near the surface on a clear, calm night frequently leads to the creation of a temperature *inversion,* i.e., a lapse rate of *increasing* temperature with height.

(3) *Radiative cooling aloft.* Clouds are quite effective blankets, retain-

ing the heat of the air below them. The loss of heat at the *tops* of clouds, though, can lead to greater instability within the clouds.

(4) *Vertical displacements of layers.* When an entire layer of air sinks (*subsidence*), the difference in the per cent compression between the bottom and top of the layer leads to a greater warming of the upper portion than of the lower portion of the layer, and therefore greater stability. Inversions created in this manner are known as *subsidence inversions.* Conversely, when a layer of air is lifted *dry* adiabatically, its stability decreases. However, if part of the layer becomes saturated during the ascent, the situation changes. If the upper portion becomes saturated before the lower, then the stability will be increased, because the upper zone will cool at a lesser rate during the ascent. But if the lower portion becomes saturated earlier, then, because the upper part will cool faster than the lower, the instability within the layer will be enhanced. Thus, instability is more likely to occur in a layer of air if the bottom of the layer is more nearly saturated at the onset of lifting.

Stability and Clouds

Cumuliform clouds are associated with instability and strong vertical motion. The convective ascent of air in such clouds appears to occur in bursts or bubbles, somewhat like those that form in boiling water. Each successive bubble, having dimensions of up to a few kilometers in the horizontal and a few hundred meters in the vertical, rises, expands, and cools; but, as the bubble ascends through the atmosphere it is "eroded" or mixed with the surroundings, gradually losing its identity (Fig. 3-16). In this way, puffs

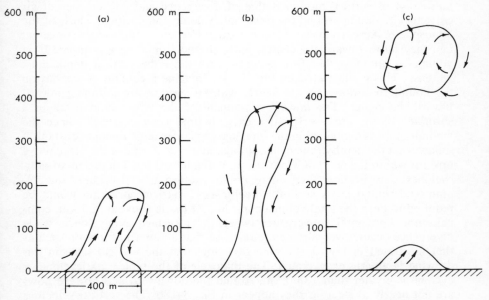

Fig. 3-16. Development of convective bubbles producing a "thermal." (Note that the vertical scale is exaggerated.)

of cumulus may form, gradually disappear, and perhaps be replaced by new puffs. Horizontal winds may carry each bubble downstream from the surface point where it was created. Strong, turbulent flow tends to cause more rapid erosion.

However, if the horizontal winds and turbulent mixing are not too great, previous bubbles may still remain while new bubbles are being formed. Then, each subsequent bubble will be able to ascend to ever greater heights, causing the cumulus cloud to develop vertically. Of course, an air bubble cannot rise without some other air descending to replace it, since there can be no vacuum. With increased instability, enhanced by the release of latent heat within the cloud, the "percolation" becomes more continuous and a well-defined thermal circulation, such as occurs in the towering cumulonimbus of a thunderstorm cell, may develop. The rapidity with which such a convective cell can develop is illustrated in the photographs of Fig. 3-17.

Columns of rising air are sometimes called *thermals*. Glider pilots learn to seek out these thermals and then try to remain within their boundaries so they can be carried upward. All around the thermal there is a compensating downward flow of air.

CAUSES OF VERTICAL MOTION

Vertical displacements of air result from "dynamic" causes as well as from changes in static stability. One dynamic cause is that of mountains which act as barriers to horizontal air flow, forcing it to ascend along the windward sides and descend on the lee sides. On a large scale, another important cause of vertical motion is that of divergence and convergence of air currents circulating around the great anticyclonic and cyclonic whirls of the atmosphere. Air currents spiraling inward at low levels of cyclones converge; i.e., they move toward the center. Since the horizontal area occupied by a volume of air must therefore decrease with time, the vertical depth must increase. This is illustrated by Fig. 3-18a. Imagine a column of air, having the boundaries shown in the figure, with streams of air spiraling inward toward the center. The *inward* component of the flow would result in a shrinking of the cross-sectional area with time (*convergence*). Since the amount of mass contained in the imaginary cylinder must remain constant, it follows that the depth of the cylinder must increase. Air must therefore move upward within the column. Conversely, in the lowest few kilometers of anticyclones, outward flow everywhere would result in an expansion of the column's horizontal cross section (*divergence*); vertical shrinking would be required to keep the total volume constant. At levels above 6 or 7 km, compensating horizontal convergence occurs over surface anticyclones, while divergence occurs over surface cyclones, so that a pattern of motion such as that illustrated in Fig. 3-18b emerges. Note that the vertical scale in this drawing is greatly exaggerated. The diameter of the typical anticyclone or cyclone is greater than 1,000 km, so that the downward and upward flows are not nearly as steep as they appear in Fig. 3-18b. The vertical velocities produced by these large-scale patterns of divergence and convergence are

Fig. 3-17. **Stages of development of a cumulonimbus over Arizona. (Courtesy of L. Battan, University of Arizona.)**

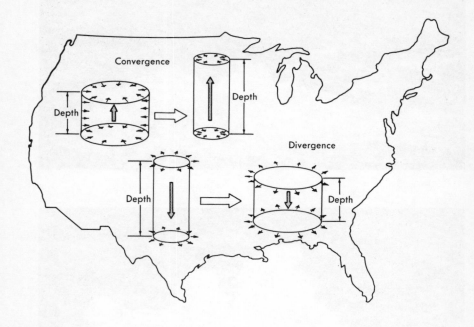

Fig. 3-18 (a). **Illustrating convergence and divergence of a disk of air.**

usually not more than a few centimeters per second (1 mile per day). However, they are sufficient to set the weather "stage" over large areas. In the absence of other influences, the weather over areas dominated by cyclones tends to be that of widespread cloudiness and precipitation, while that over anticyclonic areas is frequently clear.

SCALES OF MOTION

In previous sections of this book, it has been shown that temperature differences produce the basic force that drives the winds. However, the picture of the air flow is made complex by the earth's rotation, frictional drag and turbulence, mountain obstacles, and, perhaps most of all, the extremely variable character of the earth's surface and the incessant changes of the state of water in the air. To simplify the analysis of the enormously complex patterns of "eddies within eddies" that exist in the atmosphere, it is convenient to categorize circulation systems according to size. Almost every size is represented in the atmosphere: everything from the very small whirls that kick up the dust on a road to enormous oscillations that have wavelengths of several thousand kilometers. All of these different sizes—or *scales*

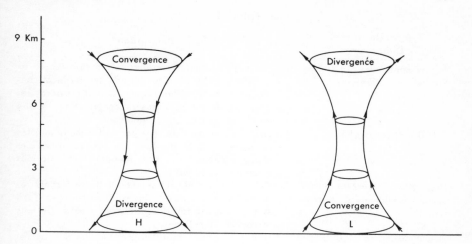

Fig. 3-18 (b). **Large-scale patterns of divergence and convergence.**

of motion, as they are called—are interdependent. For example, an eddy produced by a hill might not occur unless there was a prevailing wind due to a circulation of much larger size.

An instantaneous snapshot of the winds of the entire atmosphere would present an extremely chaotic view of the flow. The complex distribution of forces producing such flow would make prediction an impossible task. To achieve some order, a type of filtering, according to size of flow elements, must be applied. This is accomplished by a system of averaging.

The very small-scale eddies or whirls that cause a wind vane to oscillate rapidly or branches of a bush to sway with periods of perhaps only a few seconds can be eliminated by averaging the observed wind velocity over periods of several minutes. If one were to average the wind velocity over an entire day, then wind oscillations having periods of much less than a day would disappear from the record. Meteorological observations are averaged both over time and space to isolate the various sizes of atmospheric motions. The analyst of the weather maps that are published in the newspapers applies an averaging process—a smoothing of isobars—that eliminates most irregularities smaller than about 100 km.

Actually, most routine meteorological measurements are made in such a way that very small eddies are eliminated. Most anemometers and thermometers do not react to small, high-frequency changes. Observations are so widely spaced, both in time and area, that most must be considered averages over horizontal distances of tens of kilometers and vertical distances of tens of meters. Even such relatively large circulation phenomena as thunderstorms and tornadoes often fall through the "mesh" of the usual weather station network.

The scales of atmospheric motions can be classified as shown in Table 3-1.

Table 3-1

Typical Horizontal Dimension	Description
A few centimeters to a few kilometers (*microscale*)	Small high-frequency eddies, often referred to as turbulence, that are strongly affected by local conditions of both terrain roughness and temperature. Very significant as diffusers of pollutants in the air. Coriolis force is not significant.
1-100 km (*mesoscale*)	Small convective cells that persist for many minutes or hours, such as the land-sea breeze, mountain-valley breeze, tornadoes, thunderstorms. Coriolis force generally not important.
Hundreds to several thousands of kilometers (*macroscale*)	The cyclones and anticyclones that are largely responsible for the day-to-day weather changes. Such systems persist for days or even weeks. Coriolis force very significant.
Few thousand to 10,000 km (*large macroscale*)	Features of the atmospheric circulation that persist for weeks or months. Long waves that exist in this flow move very slowly or not at all across the earth. These play an important role in the characteristics of weather over periods of a month or more. Coriolis force very important.

The wind observed at any place can then be thought of as a composite of several different scales of motion. The macroscale flow patterns are associated with the large features of the earth's surface and distribution of heat: continents and oceans, extensive mountain ranges, latitudinal variations of insolation. The various scales of motion can also be characterized by the magnitude of the vertical motion associated with each. Macroscale motion is mostly in the horizontal: The vertical displacements attributable to the very large circulation features are no more than 1 or 2 cm sec^{-1} (0.02 – 0.04 mph); even in the great cyclonic storms that regularly affect the middle and high latitudes, average vertical displacements are only of the order of 50 cm sec^{-1} (1 mph). In the smaller, more intense mesoscale circulations, the vertical velocities are more comparable to the horizontal velocities; in a thunderstorm, e.g., the vertical motion is often 10 m sec^{-1} (22 mph) and can reach 30 m sec^{-1} or more. Winds of the microscale are generally much weaker than those of the larger sized motions, but the vertical motions are very nearly equal to those in the horizontal. However, microscale motions, unlike those of the mesoscale, appear to occur principally in a rather shallow layer adjacent to the earth's surface.

SMALL-SCALE THERMAL CIRCULATIONS

Small-scale circulations (mesoscale) can be roughly classified as those that extend over horizontal distances of less than 100 km and over vertical distances of several kilometers. Generally, in such small circulations, the effect of the Coriolis force can be ignored. A few examples of these are the following:

Land and Sea Breezes

A coastline is a sharp boundary between surfaces having greatly different temperature variations. The sea, because it is constantly being stirred, has a relatively small diurnal temperature change compared to the adjacent land surface. As a result, a large temperature difference can develop across the coastline during certain times of the day. In the tropics throughout the year, and at higher latitudes during the summer, the land-sea temperature gradient on a fairly calm, clear afternoon can reach 15°C over a distance of less than 50 km. At night, the temperature difference may be reversed (ocean warmer than land), although normally not nearly so pronounced.

These land-sea temperature differences lead to the creation of a thermal circulation such as that shown in Fig. 3-3. (Substitute the words "land" and "sea" for "south" and "north," respectively, for daytime; and reverse them for nighttime conditions.) The daytime landward flow is known as a *sea breeze,* while the seaward flow at night is called a *land breeze.*

The sea breeze usually begins to develop three or four hours after sunrise. In the tropics it may occur all year round, but at higher latitudes it is mostly a summer phenomenon. By 1 or 2 P.M., when it has reached its peak intensity, the circulation cell usually extends both inland and seaward about 20 km, although it has been found to penetrate inland as much as 60 or 70 km. The entire circulation cell, including the upper, seaward flow, is not normally more than 1 km deep, although in the tropics it may reach to 3 km or more. The surface wind is usually gusty and constantly shifting in direction. As the forward edge of the sea breeze passes over a point in its landward penetration, the relative humidity increases and the temperature decreases sharply (the former by 40 per cent or more, and the latter 5°C or more in less than an hour). Sometimes fog or low stratus clouds may accompany the sea breeze; there are places where the coastal water is extremely cold, such as along the Peruvian coast, where the forward edge of the sea breeze is so sharply defined that the fog appears as a solid wall.

As the land cools in the evening, the sea breeze dies, and between about 7 and 10 P.M., there is little evidence of it. The land breeze, much weaker than its daytime counterpart, will normally begin at 10 or 11 P.M. and reach its maximum development near sunrise. The principal effect of the land breeze is to prevent the air over the land from cooling quite as much as it otherwise might.

The sea breeze plays an important role in moderating the temperature of narrow strips of land along seacoasts and lake fronts. The breeze created by lakes is generally much less intense, and has a smaller width and depth. Along the shores of the Great Lakes, for example, the inland penetration is usually not more than a few kilometers. However, it offers a welcome relief from the summer heat for residents who live close to the shore.

Mountain and Valley Winds

Along mountains slopes, a thermal circulation occurs that also has a diurnal cycle. During the daytime, from about three hours after sunrise until sunset, an upslope wind, called a valley wind, blows. Between about midnight and sunrise, an opposite, downslope wind, called a mountain wind, occurs. The mountain-valley winds are most pronounced on clear, summer days, when the prevailing winds are weak.

The mountain-valley circulation is produced because the air in contact with the slope is either warmer and less dense (daytime) or cooler and denser (nighttime) than air at the same elevation over the valley. As a result, the air over the slopes rises during the day and sinks at night. Of course, the intensity of the flow and the specific direction at any point depends on the degree of slope and the configuration of the valley. Mountain and valley winds are best developed in wide, deep valleys.

The rising air currents along mountain slopes are a familiar phenomenon to every mountain climber. Frequently, cumulus clouds and showers form over summits in the ascending, expanding air. The depth of these rising currents above the slopes is usually between 100 and 200 m.

All downslope, drainage-type winds are referred to as *katabatic* winds. Most are weak, usually not exceeding 4 or 5 m/sec (10 mph), and are significant primarily because they cause cold air to drain into the valley, producing lower night temperatures in the valley than on the mountainside.

There are some very strong drainage (katabatic) winds, but most of these are set into motion by the large-scale or prevailing flow. One of the strongest of these, the glacier wind, may attain destructive violence. It occurs when air is cooled as it moves across snow fields on high plateaus: at the edge of the plateau the air cascades downward. At some places, such as along the fjorded coasts of Norway, Greenland, and Alaska, deep canyons channel the flow, thus augmenting the speed considerably. These winds blow during both the day and night. Another example is the *bora* wind, which sporadically brings in cold air down rather steep slopes to the usually warm Adriatic Sea. The bora is an intermittent wind, gusts of 50 to 60 m/sec being interspersed with calms. Where it reaches the sea, it produces great waves and kicks up spray in great quantities. A similar cold wind, the *mistral,* occurs along the French Mediterranean coast.

Föhn or Chinook

The *föhn* wind is a downslope wind that occurs in many mountainous areas, but it is not caused by drainage of dense air. It is a warm, very dry, erratic wind that sometimes appears along the lee slopes of a mountain ridge. It occurs when the prevailing winds in warm, moist air are directed against a mountain. The forced ascent causes thick clouds to form and, on occasion, heavy orographic precipitation. During most of the ascent, cooling proceeds at the *moist* adiabatic rate (4° or 5°C per km) and by the time the air reaches the peak level, much of its moisture has been removed. After crossing the ridge line, some of the air descends along the lee slopes, warming at the *dry* adiabatic rate (10°C per km). When it arrives near the bottom of the mountain, the air is very warm and dry, having been heated by the latent heat of condensation.

Although föhn winds are observed along many mountain ranges in the world, some of the most extreme cases occur along the eastern slopes of the Rocky Mountains. Here the phenomenon usually goes by the name of *chinook*, the Indian territory from which they seemed to come. The Indians commonly referred to it as the "snow eater" because its extreme dryness and warmth could melt and evaporate as much as 2 feet of snow in a day. The chinook wind frequently forces out the cold air that lies along the eastern slopes and the temperature has been observed to rise by 50°F to 60°F in half a day after its arrival.

THE MONSOON

A large-scale example of a thermal circulation is the *monsoon*. Derived from the Arabic word for season, it refers to a wind circulation that is seasonal in character. During the winter, when continents are colder than the oceans, air flows outward from the continents; while during the summer, when the continents are warmer than the oceans, the flow is inward.

Seasonal precipitation amounts are closely linked to the monsoon at places where the circulation is well developed, as in the Asian continent. The summer monsoon brings in moist oceanic air to the continent, where it rises, leading to condensation. But in the winter monsoon, precipitation is much less likely because over the continents the air is subsiding and streaming outward to the oceans.

The most intense monsoons are those produced by the large Asian land mass. The climate of southern Asia, protected from the north by the towering Himalayas, is largely determined by the monsoon. In summer, the southerly winds over the northern Indian Ocean deposit the heaviest rainfall in the world along the southern Himalayan slopes. In winter, the prevailing northeast winds are dry and there is little rain. The onset and duration of the summer monsoon are of great significance to agriculture in southern Asia. The geographic distribution, intensity, and duration vary considerably from year to year. Recently, meteorologists have launched an intensive investigation of the causes for these fluctuations, although they still cannot be forecast with any degree of certainty.

The North American continent also experiences a monsoon circulation, although it is not nearly as strong as the Asian one and tends to be obscured by migratory cyclones and fronts. Its most noticeable effect is that, in summer, the hot interior draws in moist tropical air from the Gulf of Mexico and Caribbean Sea. The summer thunderstorms over the arid highlands of the southwest can be attributed partially to the influx of moist air from the Gulf of Mexico because of the monsoon circulation.

THE GENERAL CIRCULATION

The mean, worldwide distribution of winds is referred to as the *general circulation*. It is determined by averaging wind observations over long periods of time and thus represents the largest of the scales of motion.

If the earth were not rotating and if the surface were homogeneous, the temperature difference between equator and poles would produce a thermal circulation cell in each hemisphere like that shown in Fig. 3-3. Near the surface of the earth, air would flow equatorward; heated by the warmth of the equatorial regions, it would rise and gradually move poleward, where it would sink, thus completing the circuit. Earth rotation and the non-uniform surface properties greatly modify this simple circulation pattern. Instead of one single cell in each hemisphere, there are three latitudinal cells and there are longitudinal variations around each hemisphere.

A schematic representation of the flow averaged over each latitude of the globe is shown in Fig. 3-19. The horizontal flow is shown within the circle,

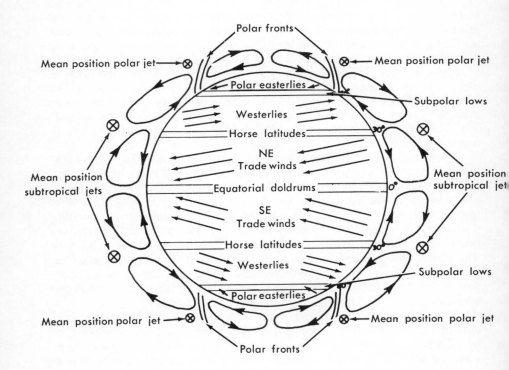

Fig. 3-19.   Schematic representation of the general circulation of atmosphere.

while the net meridional circulation is depicted in the vertical cross section around the periphery. Near the equator there is a belt of low pressure; it is known as the *doldrums,* because the horizontal pressure gradient is generally weak here and winds are light and variable. It marks a zone where the wind belts to the north and south converge and rise. As a result, there are frequent heavy rain showers in the doldrums.

The 30°-wide belts to the south and north of the doldrums are noted for the remarkable persistence of the low-level winds. Winds from the east dominate both of these belts, the one in the Northern Hemisphere experiencing winds generally from the northeast, while southeast winds are found in the Southern Hemisphere belt. These winds are known as the *trade winds* because of the important role they played in opening up the New World when ships depended on sails.

A series of large high pressure areas (anticyclones) is located at about 30°N and another near 30°S. In these zones the mean vertical motion is one of descent, which inhibits the formation of clouds and precipitation. In this belt, along the eastern edges of the individual anticyclones, most of the world's great deserts are found. The light winds generally encountered in this belt have given rise to the name popularly applied to this subtropical high pressure zone: the *horse latitudes*. Spanish sailing vessels, carrying horses to the New World, on occasion were becalmed in one of these high centers and some of the animals had to be slaughtered as the supply of food became insufficient to complete the voyage.

Between 35° and 60° in both hemispheres, westerly winds prevail. Although they vary considerably between northwest and southwest, they usually have a component from the west. This zone is noted for its large number of moving cyclones and the changeable weather.

At 60° latitude, the subpolar lows form an almost continuous trough of low pressure in the Southern Hemisphere, but in the Northern Hemisphere there are two distinct semi-permanent low centers, one near the Aleutian Islands in the Pacific, and the other near Iceland in the Atlantic. Between the subpolar lows and the poles, high pressure areas dominate close to the surface, with weak easterlies. But these yield with increased height rather quickly to westerly winds, so that much of the middle and upper troposphere poleward of about 25° is dominated by west winds.

Circulation changes with longitude, season, and altitude can be noted from the charts of Fig. 3-20. (The contours of the 500-mb pressure surface determine the wind flow in the same way as isobars do on a surface of constant elevation.) From the sea level charts, note that the subtropical high pressure belt is not continuous either in summer or in winter, but rather is broken into cells over the Atlantic and Pacific Oceans. These two cells are especially well defined in the summer. They are also displaced several degrees northward in the summer. The interiors of the North American and Asian continents produce cold high pressure areas in the winter and warm lows in the summer. The two subpolar lows—the Icelandic and the Aleutian —are well defined in winter but almost disappear in summer.

Aloft, both in winter and summer, westerlies dominate each hemisphere poleward of the horse latitudes. In winter they are much more intense than in summer, as can be seen from the closer spacing of the winter contours in Fig. 3-20b.

Not clearly evident on the 500-mb charts of Fig. 3-20 are the so-called *jet streams*. These are narrow bands of high velocity winds, imbedded in the westerlies, that meander around each hemisphere at elevations extending from 4 or 5 km to above the tropopause. Discovered in 1946, the cores of

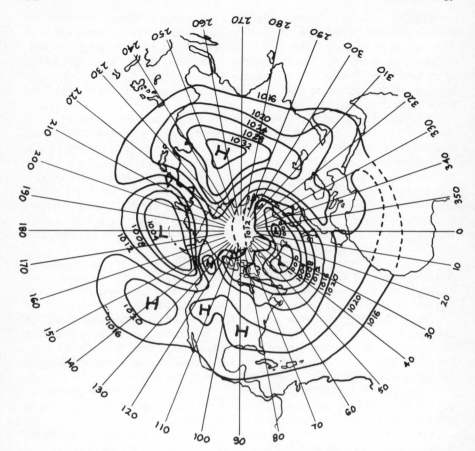

Fig. 3-20 (a).   January normal sea level pressure, Northern Hemisphere.

these "rivers" of air are usually about 100 km wide and 2 or 3 km deep, and flow at speeds as much as 100 knots faster than the air on either side of them. The location and intensity of jet streams change from day to day throughout the year, but they are associated with zones of strong horizontal temperature gradients and therefore follow closely the oscillations in position and strength of the polar front. In addition to the circumpolar jet stream, which is normally found between 35° and 60° latitude, a second, "subtropical jet stream" has been uncovered in the horse latitudes at very high elevations (9-13 km). The subtropical jet stream does not meander over such a range of latitudes as does the circumpolar jet stream.

The above discussion illustrates that the general circulation* is considerably different from that expected for a uniform, nonrotating earth. The tropi-

---

* Our knowledge of the general circulation is based on a sparse observation network. Very few observations have been made over the unpopulated areas of the earth—oceans, mountains, jungles, arctic and antarctic—which comprise most of the earth's surface.

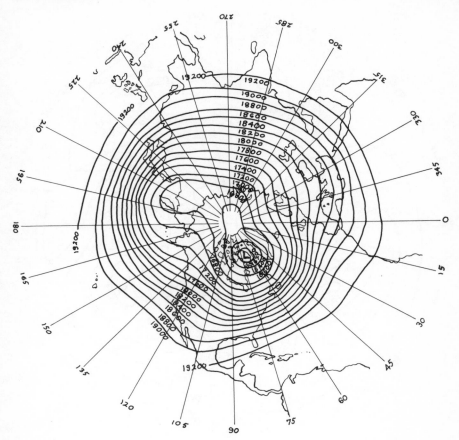

Fig. 3-20 (b). **January normal 500-mb chart, Northern Hemisphere.**

cal and the polar cells (see vertical cross section of meridional flow of Fig. 3-19) look like thermal circulation cells whose wind directions have been influenced by the earth's rotation. The air moving equatorward from the horse latitudes acquires its easterly component because of the Coriolis force, which produces a deflection to the right in the Northern Hemisphere and to the left in the Southern Hemisphere. The same reasoning can be applied to the polar easterlies. Aloft, in both the tropical and polar cells, poleward moving air would become increasingly from the west.

That a single thermal cell does not extend from equator to pole appears due to the fact that the steady "meridional" (south-north) component disappears as the flow is deflected by the Coriolis force into becoming more "zonal" (along latitude circles). The intermediate, temperate zone is thought to represent a belt in which there is no organized thermal circulation, but only frequent large eddies (cyclonic disturbances) that intermittently transport heat and momentum between the tropical and polar cells.

A study of the angular momentum of the atmosphere seems to indicate

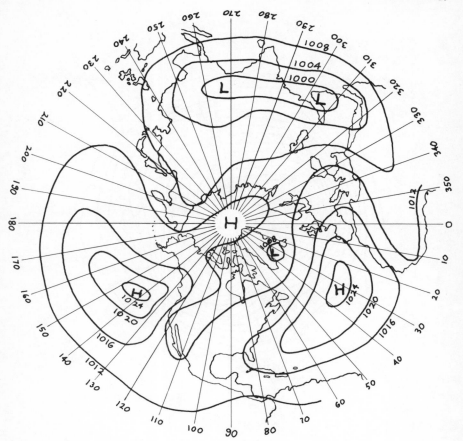

Fig. 3-20 (c).   **July normal sea level pressure, Northern Hemisphere.**

that the cyclones of the westerlies are required to prevent an accumulation of momentum over the tropics. The angular momentum of a particle of air is given by $m \times \omega \times r$, where m is its mass, ω is its angular velocity, and r the spin radius, i.e., the perpendicular distance from the earth's axis. If there are no torques (forces that cause turning, such as that applied to a pipe by a wrench), the angular momentum of a parcel will not change. Now, if a parcel of air moves from a lower to a higher latitude at a constant altitude above the earth's surface, its distance from the earth's axis (r) will decrease so that ω, the angular velocity, must increase. (This is like the skater who makes himself spin faster by pulling his arms in toward his body, thus concentrating his mass near the spin axis.) Since the earth's angular velocity is the same at all latitudes, this means that if the parcel were originally spinning at the same rate as the earth's surface, it will be spinning at a faster rate than the underlying surface when it arrives at higher latitudes. Thus, it will have acquired an additional speed from the west, relative to the earth. As an ex-

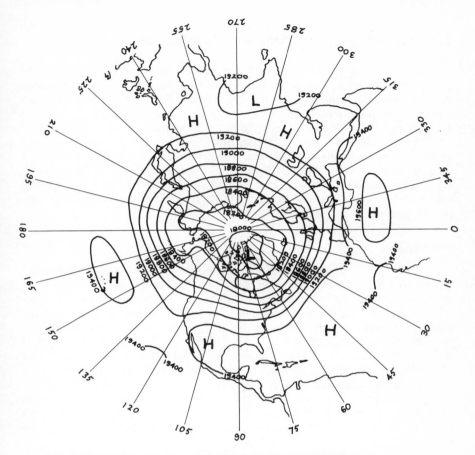

Fig. 3-20 (d).   July normal 500-mb chart, Northern Hemisphere.

ample, a parcel of air displaced from the equator to latitude 60° would increase its west-to-east velocity by about 230 m/sec (515 mph)! Such velocities are far greater than anything ever observed.

The tropical and subtropical easterlies, slowed by friction at the earth's surface, have their westerly angular momentum increased. This input of westerly angular momentum, transported a short distance poleward by the tropical cell, is gradually dissipated by the westerlies of middle latitudes, which in turn lose the acquired momentum at the surface through friction. Thus, the great cyclonic disturbances of the westerlies dissipate the excess momentum much like the small turbulent eddies near the earth's surface diffuse a high concentration of smoke in the air.

A complete picture and explanation of the general circulation has still to be achieved by meteorologists. Until our knowledge of this basic flow pattern is more advanced, the problem of long-range weather prediction is likely to remain unsolved.

AIR MASSES, FRONTS, AND WAVE CYCLONES

In the discussion of the general circulation, mention was made of the importance of the large, essentially horizontal eddies in producing an exchange of air between the polar regions and the tropics. These large whirls are most active in the middle latitudes, where they are the chief weather producers. Periodically (in some places, every few days in winter), these wave cyclones, as they are called by meteorologists, develop along the boundary between warm and cool streams of air, later sucking these streams of air toward their centers; in the process they transport "cold" equatorward and "heat" poleward. The prognosis of the formation and development of these cyclones is one of the principal tasks of the short-range forecaster in the polar and temperate regions of the earth.

Air Masses

An *air mass* is a huge body of air, extending over thousands of kilometers, within which the temperature and humidity change gradually in the horizontal; i.e., there are no sharp horizontal changes of temperature or humidity. Air masses are created principally within the anticyclonic flow of the subtropical and polar high pressure belts. The air circulates slowly in these systems over surfaces of fairly uniform properties and gradually acquires thermal and moisture characteristics representative of these surfaces. For example, the air flowing around the semi-permanent Atlantic anticyclone very quickly acquires the warmth and moisture of such water bodies as the Caribbean and Gulf of Mexico. Cold air masses, such as those that form over the frozen surfaces of northern Canada in winter, take somewhat longer to form, but under fairly stagnant conditions horizontal homogeneity can exist to a 3- or 4-km depth.

Air masses are classified according to their source region: *polar* or *tropical, maritime* or *continental*. The chief air masses that affect the weather of North America are continental polar (*cP*), maritime polar (*mP*), and maritime tropical (*mT*). The origin of continental polar air masses is northern Canada. In winter, the *cP* air mass is dry and stable before it moves out, but when it moves southward over the United States it is heated from below and its stability decreases. The portion that traverses the Great Lakes picks up moisture, which frequently results in snow showers along the eastern shores of the lakes and in the Appalachian Mountains. Occasionally, this *cP* air may penetrate the Rocky Mountain range.

The maritime tropical air that affects the United States generally comes from the Gulf of Mexico. In winter, maritime polar air sweeping out of the Pacific is largely responsible for the winter rains of the west coast of the United States. As it strikes the coastal range and then the Rockies, the forced lifting causes heavy rain and snow over these barriers.

After it has left its source region, an air mass can be further characterized by its temperature relative to the surface over which it is traveling. An air mass is said to be *cold* if it is colder than the underlying surface and *warm* if it is warmer than the surface. A cold air mass will be heated from below, so that the lapse rate will increase, while a warm air mass will lose heat to the underlying surface and its lapse rate will decrease (it will become more stable).

Fronts

Across a boundary separating air masses of differing properties there would exist a sharp contrast of temperature and humidity. Such a boundary, where air masses "clash," is called a *frontal zone* or, more commonly, a *front*. The name "front" was coined by the Norwegian meteorologists who first developed the polar front theory during World War I, possibly because the oscillations of the boundary, with periodic flareups of weather along it, reminded them of the long battle line in Europe with its intermittent activity.

The front separating two air masses slopes upward over the cold, denser air. This is illustrated in Fig. 3-21, a typical vertical cross section of fronts

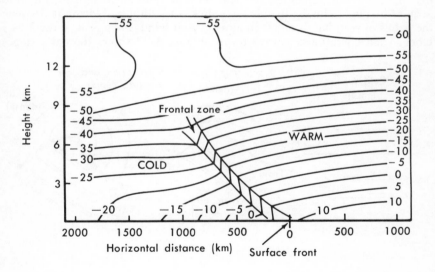

Fig. 3-21. **Vertical cross section of a front (isotherms: °C).**

over the center of the North American continent. Note that the vertical scale is greatly exaggerated. The average slope of fronts is only about 1:150, ranging from as little as 1:250 to as steep as 1:50. The width of the front—the transition zone between air masses—is usually about 50–100 km, but on the scale of distances that we are considering, such a width is closely approximated by the thickness of a heavy line drawn on a weather map.

The boundary between the warm and cold air masses must always slope upward over the cold air. This is because the cold air is denser fluid. (Imagine two fluids such as water and oil, side by side, separated by a partition. If the partition is removed, the heavier water will slide beneath the oil.) Now if either the warm air is moving against the wedge of cold air or the wedge is pushing under the warm air, there will be forced lifting. In either case, cooling due to expansion may lead to condensation and possibly precipitation over the frontal surface.

Wave Cyclones

The weather pattern associated with migratory cyclonic depressions of the middle latitudes has been known for about 80 years. The polar front model associated the formation and maturation of these storms with undulations of the frontal boundary. A front separates air masses of different densities. The air masses flowing side by side may develop zones of strong wind "shear" between them; i.e., the currents of air on both sides of the boundary may have different velocities. In such an event, both air currents will tend to acquire a spin. (This is like giving a stick a rotation by placing it between the palms of your hands and then moving your hands in opposite directions.) Under such conditions, a wave forms. Figure 3-22 shows the early stages

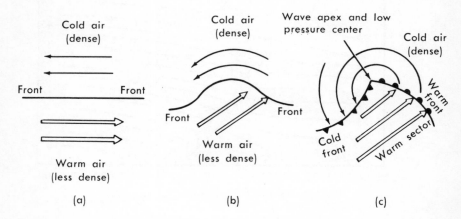

Fig. 3-22. **Genesis and early development of a wave cyclone (Northern Hemisphere).**

of development, looking down on the surface of the earth (Northern Hemisphere).

The theory of the development of this wave is rather complex. It is a combination of many types of undulations, such as "gravity waves"—those that you see in water when you disturb the surface by dropping a stone in it; shearing waves, such as those formed when wind blows along a water surface; and inertial waves (Fig. 3-8). It turns out that for certain wavelengths (the overall length of the disturbance) these composite oscillations are unstable and the wave grows in amplitude and circulation intensity. Waves having lengths between about 600 and 3,000 km are unstable and these are the ones that experience development beyond stage (b) of Fig. 3-22.

As the wave develops, low pressure forms at its apex (Fig. 3-22c) and both the warm and cold currents move in a cyclonic pattern around it. To the left (in the figure) of the apex, the front is advancing toward the warm air and this segment of the front is called the *cold front*; to the right of the apex, the front is receding from the warm air and so this segment is called the *warm front*. The warm air between the fronts is known as the *warm sector*.

Figure 3-23 represents an idealized wave cyclone, the view looking

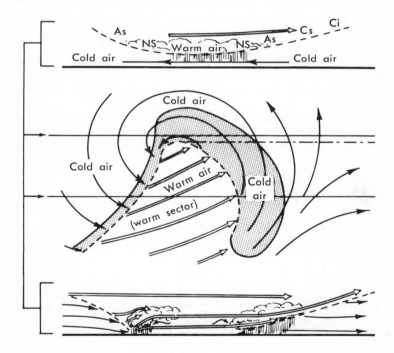

Fig. 3-23. The wave cyclone model. (After J. Bjerknes and H. Solberg.) Center drawing: horizontal plane view. Top: vertical cross-sectional view just north of wave apex. Bottom: vertical cross-sectional view across warm sector. (For abbreviations of cloud type names, see page 20.)

downward on the earth shown in the center and vertical cross sections taken a little south (bottom drawing) and a little north (top) of the apex. Imagine the entire system moving toward the right (eastward), as they normally do. If you were standing to the east and south of the apex, ahead of the warm front, the first sign of the approaching system would be high cirrus clouds. As time goes on, the wisps of cirrus thicken to cirrostratus clouds; these often cause halos (rings around the sun or moon), a sure sign of rain within 24 hours, according to a well-known proverb. Gradually the clouds lower and thicken to altostratus. The pressure falls, and the wind increases and backs (changes direction in a counterclockwise direction), as the low center gets closer. The temperature begins to rise slowly as the frontal transition zone approaches. Within 300 km of the surface position of the front, precipitation begins, either in the form of rain or snow. After the warm front passes, the precipitation stops, the wind veers (changes direction in a clockwise direction) and the pressure stops falling. Within the warm sector, the weather depends largely on the stability of the warm air mass and the surface over which it is moving; there may be showers or almost clear skies.

The type of weather accompanying the passage of the cold front depends on the sharpness of the front, its speed, and the stability of the air being forced aloft. Usually there are towering cumulus and showers along the forward edge of the front. Sometimes, especially in the midwest during the spring, severe *squalls* precede the front. But in other cases, nimbostratus and rain extend over a zone of 75-100 km. After the frontal passage, the wind veers sharply and the pressure begins to rise. Within a short distance behind the cold front, the weather clears, the temperature begins to fall, and the visibility greatly improves.

The early genesis stages of the wave cyclone shown in Fig. 3-22 normally take between 12 and 24 hours. Subsequent development of the wave, shown in Fig. 3-24, takes an additional two or three days. As the wave breaks,

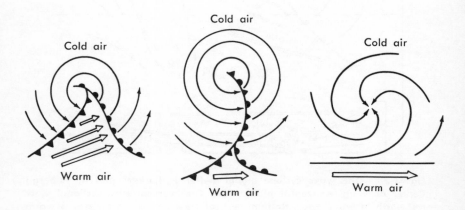

Fig. 3-24. **Later stages in the development of a wave cyclone (Northern Hemisphere).**

the cold front begins to overtake the warm front. This process is called *occlusion* and the resulting boundary an *occluded front*. The vertical cross sections of Fig. 3-25 illustrate that either the cold front can move up along the warm

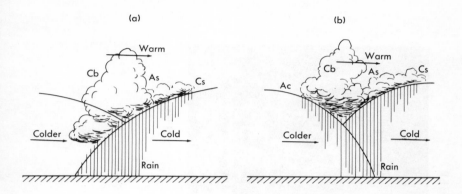

Fig. 3-25. **Vertical cross section of occlusions. (a) Warm-front type (b) Cold-front type.**

front (warm-front type occlusion) or it can force itself under the warm front (cold-front type). The occluded front is the boundary that separates the two cold air masses.

The shorter wave disturbances—those less than 500 km wavelength—are gradually damped out by friction. They usually do not last longer than 36 hours; the low center near the apex is weak, and any weather they produce is confined to a narrow zone along the frontal boundary.

During most of the wave cyclone's history it is in an occluded state. Gradually, the fronts begin to dissolve as the kinetic energy of the whirl is dissipated by friction and the winds subside.

The maximum intensity of the wave cyclone, in terms of horizontal pressure gradient and wind velocity, normally occurs during the occlusion process. This happens because occlusion produces a redistribution of the air masses: The denser, cold air moves in at the surface of the system and less dense, warm air is forced aloft. This change in the distribution of mass within the eddy results in a loss of potential energy (more light air aloft, and more heavy air below) which reappears as kinetic energy—winds. Of course, the whirl is continuously being slowed by surface friction and thus losing some of its kinetic energy. When, in the last stages of the cyclone's history, there is little further readjustment of air masses and the supply of kinetic energy is cut off, friction gradually brings the giant eddy to a stop.

The net effect of the wave cyclone's history is to disrupt the initial air mass distribution. Part of the cold air mass is swept to lower latitudes near the surface, while some of the warm air mass is transported to higher latitudes aloft.

The sequence of events associated with wave cyclones—as described above—is, of course, an idealization. Few wave cyclones adhere closely to the model throughout their development. However, the model does serve as a guide in furthering understanding of these vortices.

FIRST COMPLETE VIEW OF THE WORLD'S WEATHER

TIROS IX

FEBRUARY 13, 1965

Fig. 3-26.   Mosaic of Tiros satellite photographs with superimposed weather map. (Courtesy of NASA.)

OTHER VORTICES IN THE ATMOSPHERE

The large, extratropical *wave cyclones* of middle and high latitudes are the largest weather-producing vortices, but usually not the most violent. Two of these—the tropical cyclone and the tornado—are the most destructive of natural phenomena, except, possibly, for earthquakes. Fortunately, the tropical cyclone, which averages about 700 km (450 miles) in diameter (compared to the extratropical cyclone's average diameter of 2,500 km), spends most of its life on the oceans where it can do little harm; and the tornado, although it packs a tremendous punch, is very small (average diameter of less than a quarter of a mile) and rarely lasts longer than 1 or 2 hours. The details of formation and structure of both of these violent vortices are incompletely known, largely because of inadequate observations: In the case of the tropical cyclone, the reports over oceans are too scanty to properly pin down the dynamics, while tornadoes are so small and have such a short duration that they usually fall between the observation points of the normal land network of stations.

Tropical Cyclones

Tropical cyclones, as their name implies, are cyclonic whirlpools that are formed over the tropics. In fact, they almost invariably form over the oceans in the latitudes between about 5° and 20° from the equator. They are spawned over all of the tropical oceans except the South Atlantic. Each area of the world has its own local name for this storm, the most common being: *hurricane* (North America), *typhoon* (eastern Asia), *cyclone* (India), *willy willy* (Australia), *baguio* (China Sea). Figure 3-27 gives the more common

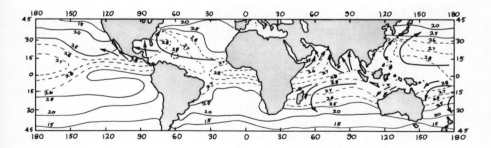

Fig. 3-27. Paths of tropical cyclones (normal sea surface isotherms in °C). (After Palmén.)

points of origin and paths of tropical cyclones in the world. In the discussion that follows we will use the term which is commonly used in the United States for these storms: hurricane.

A bird's-eye view of a hurricane, taken from a weather satellite, is shown in Fig. 3-28. Note how the bands of clouds spiral in a counterclockwise direction inward toward the center (Northern Hemisphere). From this photo-

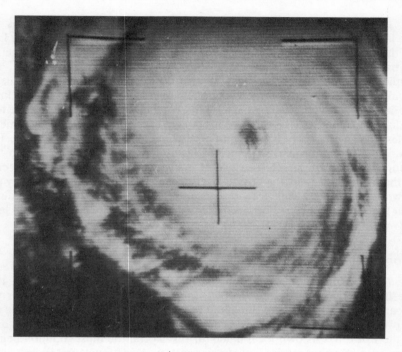

Fig. 3-28. Satellite photograph of a hurricane. (Courtesy of NASA.)

graph alone, one could hardly imagine the violence within it. Figure 3-29 presents a picture of the weather conditions in a typical hurricane. (Only a part of the left half is shown, but since hurricanes are approximately circular in form, the conditions on the right would be repeated on the left.) The weather that normally can be expected during the approach and passage of a hurricane can be determined by imagining the observer moving slowly (usually 10-15 mph) from the outer edge to the center (right to left), and then out to the edge again.

High clouds, which are not too common over the tropical oceans, usually appear 200-300 miles in advance of the hurricane. The pressure begins to fall slowly and the winds begin to pick up above the normal 10-20 mph of the trade winds. Within 200 miles of the center, the winds reach gale force (about 30 mph), steadily increasing in speed, and the pressure begins to fall off a little more rapidly. By the time the observer is within 100 miles of the center, the winds will be 50 mph or more, the clouds will be low and menacing, and the pressure will be falling rapidly. Rain usually starts falling 60 or 70 miles from the center and increases in intensity until it is coming down in torrents at 20 or 30 miles from the center. Winds in this last zone may be as high as 200 mph.

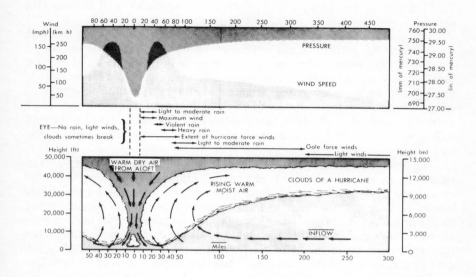

Fig. 3-29. **Vertical sections of a hurricane.**

If the center of the storm passes over the observer, he has a truly startling experience. This center is known as the *eye* of the hurricane. Quite abruptly, the winds decrease from 150 mph or more to less than 20 mph in a distance of 15 miles or less. (This distance corresponds to a time interval of less than an hour for the typical hurricane movement.) The rain stops completely, the clouds become thin, and the sun may shine through breaks. The clouds surrounding the eye appear as nearly vertical walls, extending from 2,000 or 3,000 ft to 40,000 ft or more. This is but a respite from the monster storm. Soon, the other half of the "doughnut" will strike and the observer will experience weather conditions similar to those encountered before, except that they will occur in reverse order and the wind direction will be opposite.

The West Indies hurricane season extends from June through November, although most hurricanes occur during August, September, and October. During the 72-year period of 1887 to 1958, a total of 331 hurricanes (an average of 4.6 per year) were reported in the North Atlantic and adjoining waters, in addition to 241 other tropical cyclones that did not reach hurricane intensity (officially, having wind speeds greater than 73 mph). About 4 per cent of these occurred in the month of June, 6 per cent in July, 29 per cent in August, 36 per cent in September, 19 per cent in October, and 3 per cent in November; there were only five hurricanes in the other six months of the year. The number of tropical cyclones per year has ranged from as few as two to as many as twenty-one. In the United States, it is customary to identify each season's hurricanes by giving them girls' names in alphabetical succession; thus, the destructive storms of 1963 were Arlene (the first), Cindy (the third), Edith (the fifth), Flora (the sixth and most devastating, causing over

7,000 deaths in Haiti and Cuba), Ginny (the seventh), and Helena (the eighth).

The average lifetime of a West Indies hurricane is nine days, although those occurring during August appear to be more durable, lasting for an average of twelve days. Hurricanes tend to move in the direction of the flow in which they are imbedded, much like an eddy in a river moves downstream. During their early stages, in the Atlantic, while they are still well within the easterly winds, they tend to move toward the west or northwest. If they reach north of about 30° latitude before dissipating, they get caught by the prevailing west winds of the middle latitudes, and are swept toward the northeast.

Hurricanes sometimes move in a very erratic fashion. For example, Hurricane Flora (October, 1963) meandered about over eastern Cuba for almost five days and Hurricane Betsy (September, 1965) started toward the northwest over the Bahamas and then passed through the Florida Strait, finally crashing into Louisiana. Although the average speed of hurricanes is about 12 mph, the speeds of individual storms are extremely variable; when they get caught up in the usual west winds north of 30° latitude, they frequently greatly accelerate, sometimes achieving a speed of over 50 mph.

The hurricane is a powerhouse of energy. Circulating hundreds of millions of tons of air at speeds of up to 200 mph or more, the average hurricane generates 300-400 billion kilowatt-hours of energy per day, about 200 times the total electrical power produced in the United States. An average hurricane precipitates 10-20 billion tons of water each day.

The warm, moisture-laden air of the tropical oceans possesses an enormous capacity for heat energy, and it is estimated that most of the energy required to create and sustain a hurricane comes from what is released through condensation. A hurricane is an unusually organized, very large convection system that pumps great amounts of warm, moist air to high levels of the atmosphere at very rapid rates. The arrows in the vertical cross section of Fig. 3-29 illustrate the overall convection pattern within a fully-developed hurricane. Warm, moist air rises sharply in the ring between 10 and 50 miles of the center. New air flows in toward the center from hundreds of miles away. If the air starts out with even a slight counterclockwise rotary motion (this is thought to be caused by the Coriolis force), it will spin faster and faster as it nears the center.

Most meteorologists agree that some sort of "priming" is needed to start the flow of the hurricane. Wavelike motions in the trade winds that look something like Fig. 3-30a, may start the hurricane's development. Within a day or so, the circulation touched off by the wave may take on the appearance shown in Fig. 3-30b and, if it continues to develop, the flow may become a tight spiral, as illustrated in Fig. 3-30c. At this stage the hurricane is born.

The greatest damage and loss of life during hurricanes results from flooding of coastal areas by the ocean surges and waves caused by the wind. The sea is in an agitated state hundreds or even thousands of miles from the storm center. When wind blows along a water surface it exerts a frictional drag on the water that results in ripples or "waves." The wind drag increases with higher wind speed and so does the size of the waves generated. During

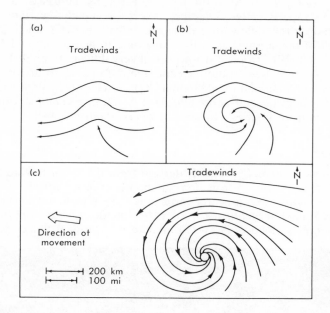

Fig 3-30. **Development of a hurricane from an easterly wave.**

a hurricane, air travels at high speed over long distances, producing waves of great height. The wave heights (vertical distance from crest to valley) often reach 35 ft and sometimes exceed 50 ft in the zone of strong winds. As waves move out from under the winds that generated them, the crests decrease in height and become more regular in shape. Waves of similar height and length between consecutive crests tend to move in groups. These composite waves are known as *swells,* and they can travel thousands of miles from the generating area with little loss of energy. When these swells approach a coast, the varying depth to the ocean bottom and the irregularities of the coastline complicate the wave structure. Sometimes very steep waves travel up estuaries, damaging vessels and piers. If these swells coincide with the normal high tide of the area, they may cause extensive flood damage.

However, the really damaging effects of the wind-churned ocean are not felt until the hurricane center is within a hundred miles or so of the coast. Rapid rises in the water level, known as *surges,* result from a piling up of water along the coast by the driving winds. Such "hills" of water can be 15 ft or more above normal sea level. With storm waves riding 20 ft or more above these mounds, large inland areas can be inundated. During a hurricane in 1900, Galveston, Texas, was flooded by just such a surge, which demolished the city and drowned about 5,000 persons. In 1961, when Hurricane Carla struck the Gulf coast, a surge was predicted and the affected areas were evacuated beforehand, so that there was no loss of human life.

When a hurricane moves off the ocean onto land, the frictional drag that the surface of the earth exerts on the wind is greatly increased; however, although the air speed is slowed, it takes a more direct path toward the low center. This more rapid inflow toward the center leads to the gradual dissipation or "filling" of the storm, but at the same time to heavier precipitation. Although the genesis of tropical storms is still very difficult to predict and, once formed, their movement is quite erratic, the use of aircraft and radar allow the U.S. Weather Bureau to maintain a close watch of their path and to issue advance warnings of their approach. As a result, in recent years there have been few deaths or injuries. However, property damage is high.

Tornadoes

The name *tornado* is probably derived from the Spanish word "tornar," which means "to turn." A tornado is an intense cyclonic vortex, in which the air spirals rapidly about a nearly vertical axis. Seen from a distance, it looks like a gray funnel or elephant's trunk extending downward from the base of a cumulonimbus cloud (Fig. 3-31). Where this pendant cloud reaches the

Fig. 3-31.   **Tornado. (Courtesy of ESSA.)**

ground, great masses of dust and debris circle the lowest couple of hundred feet.

The winds associated with tornadoes are too strong to be withstood by the ordinary anemometer, so there are few reliable measurements. Estimates from damage to buildings and the impact force of flying objects indicate that speeds range generally between 100 and 300 mph, although it is possible that speeds up to 500 mph can occur. Such a wind necessitates a very strong pressure gradient. The pressure drop between the outside and inside of a tornado is usually of the order of 25 mb, but falls up to 200 mb have been observed.

The lengths of tornado paths average only about 6 km, but they are extremely erratic. Some touch ground over a distance of only 20 or 30 m, while others hop and skip over tracks of hundreds of kilometers. Some tornadoes hardly move, while a few have been known to travel at a speed up to 200 km/hour (125 mph). Some last only a fraction of a minute, while others persist for several hours; the average duration is less than 10 minutes. Most move toward the east or northeast (Northern Hemisphere) but every direction of movement has been observed.

During their brief lives, tornadoes can be very destructive. A building in the path of a tornado will certainly be badly damaged, if not destroyed. The cause of the damage to buildings is threefold: the enormous force exerted by the wind, the sudden pressure difference created between the interior and the exterior of the building, and the strong upward air currents. With a rapid pressure drop of 100 mb, the net outward pressure on the walls of a building could be 200 pounds per square foot, and buildings have been observed to literally explode. Wind pressure can easily reach several hundred pounds per square foot. And powerful updrafts may lift very heavy objects. Many freak occurrences have been reported during tornadoes, such as showers of frogs that were sucked up from ponds miles away, the "defeathering" of chickens, straws driven through posts, and entire buildings carried for hundreds of meters.

Tornadoes occur infrequently. Although they have been observed in every part of the world outside of the extremely cold regions, they are most common over large continents, where strong horizontal temperature contrasts exist: in the United States east of the Rockies, in southern and middle U.S.S.R., and in southern Australia. In the United States there are about 150 per year, mostly in the central plains states. Iowa, Kansas, Arkansas, Oklahoma, and Mississippi have the highest frequency of tornadoes per unit area (Fig. 3-32). They occur principally in the afternoon during the spring, but can occur at any time during the day throughout the year.

The formation mechanism of tornadoes is still somewhat obscure. They form generally in the vicinity of intense cold fronts and *squall lines* (moving lines of thunderstorms). Marked instability is an important factor, but such conditions often exist without tornadoes being produced. Evidently there must be some special circumstances that lead to the sudden creation of a deep low pressure center before it can be filled by the inflow of surrounding air. Probably there is a combination of vertical instability, which provides the energy for the motion, and a mechanical impetus: strong shearing action of air currents in juxtaposition that creates the necessary spin. Once formed,

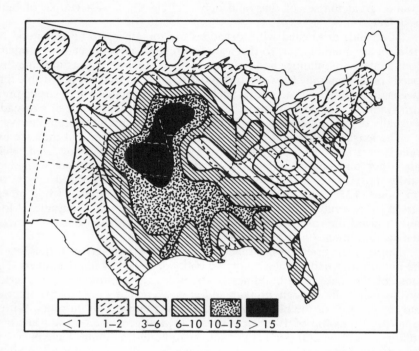

Fig 3-32. Total number of tornadoes per 50-mile square reported in the period of 1920–1949. (After Fawbush, Miller and Starrett, *Bull. Amer. Met. Soc.*, Jan. 1951.)

strong convection action will sustain the vortex until the potential energy has been dissipated and friction destroys the whirl.

Tornadoes occasionally form over warm water. Because of the high moisture content of the air, the funnels are heavily laden with water drops, so that they look somewhat like a stream of water pouring from the cloud base (Fig. 3-33). They are called, for this reason, *waterspouts*. Usually, waterspouts are not as intense as tornadoes over land. Near their base, the winds churn the water surface, producing waves and spray.

A whirlwind that frequently forms on very hot days, especially over deserts, is the *dust devil*. Normally, there are no clouds associated with these and they are no more than a whirling column of dust or sand. They are produced by strong convection near the surface, and given a rotation by slight, terrain-induced irregularities in the winds. These have been observed to rotate in both senses, clockwise and counterclockwise, with equal frequency.

THUNDERSTORMS

A *thunderstorm* is, as the name implies, a storm accompanied by thunder and, therefore, lightning. It occurs in the cumulonimbus cloud. As Benjamin

Fig. 3-33. **Waterspout over Biscayne Bay, Miami, Florida. (Courtesy of G. E. Dunn, USWB.)**

Franklin demonstrated in 1750, lightning discharges are giant electrical sparks. Cumulonimbus clouds, therefore, are great natural electrical generators. Like man-made machines, such as batteries, the cloud produces "poles" of concentrations of positive and negative electricity.

An important question that is still not adequately answered is how the powerful convective currents in these clouds produce the electrical charge and then separate the positive from the negative electricity. The lower part of a thundercloud has a concentration of negative charge, while the upper part is largely positive. The process that produces and separates charges must involve the water and ice particles in clouds. Some suggested processes are: (1) Friction between the ice particles formed near the top of such clouds would cause the ice to become negatively charged. Large ice crystals that fall would then carry negative electricity downward, leaving the upper portion positive. (2) Water droplets, when they form, tend to attract negative ions. (Ions are molecules that have become charged through the loss or gain of an electron. In the atmosphere, ions are produced by the radiations from radioactive material in the soil, by cosmic rays from the sun, and by combustion, friction, and splitting of water drops in sprays.) (3) If a cloud has already a predominance of positive charge near the top and negative near the bottom, so that an electrical potential exists, then any drop will tend to distribute its internal charge so that the bottom portion of the drop is positive and the upper portion is negative. If a current of air is sweeping upward past the drop, negative ions will be captured by the bottoms of the drops (which face the air current) more readily than will the positive ions. The rising air currents will therefore arrive near the cloud top with their negative ions depleted, or, in other words, with a positive charge.

Regardless of how the thundercloud does it, the fact remains that enormous potential differences are generated within clouds and between clouds and ground. Just before a discharge, the electrical potential gradient is of the order of 3,000 volts per centimeter and potential differences between the extremities of flashes reach hundreds of millions of volts. A typical thunderstorm dissipates electrical energy at an average rate of about a million kilowatts.

Special photographic techniques have shown that individual lightning discharges actually consist of multiple strokes, each lasting about 0.0002 sec, with about 0.0001 sec between successive strokes. The air along the lightning channel is heated momentarily to about 15,000°C (compared to the sun's surface temperature of about 6,000°C); this causes a very rapid expansion of air, which in turn results in the deep sound called *thunder*. The rumbling of thunder is due to the fact that the sound is generated over a long discharge path, so that sound waves travel over many different paths to the observer, and much of the sound is reflected. The approximate distance of a thunderstorm can be computed by noting the time elapsed between a flash of lightning and the arrival of the sound wave by using the average speed of sound (330 m/sec, or 1,080 ft/sec).

The old proverb that lightning does not strike twice in the same place is, of course, untrue. Tall towers and buildings are repeatedly struck by lightning; Franklin's lightning rod protects such structures by providing a low resistance conductor of the electrical current to the ground. One should always avoid being near an isolated, high target during a thunderstorm. Do not get caught under a tree or in an open golf course during a storm.

Figure 3-17 is a sequence of photographs that illustrates the rapid development of an Arizona cumulonimbus. Of many individual cumulus convective cells appearing on the horizon in the first photograph, one mushroomed vertically into a mature storm in only 18 minutes. It is not usual that isolated convective "cells" of this sort can be identified; normally there is a tendency for adjacent cells to develop and join together. Frequently, there are great masses or lines of thunderstorms extending over 50 miles or more, but a single "cell" has a diameter of about 5 miles.

Studies have shown that there are three characteristic stages in the life cycle of a thunderstorm cell. These are illustrated in Fig. 3-34. The initial, *cumulus* stage usually lasts for about 15 minutes. During this period, the cell grows laterally from 1 or 2 miles in diameter to 5 or 6 miles, and vertically to 25,000 or 30,000 ft. Note from Fig. 3-34a that the updraft is strongest (about 20 mph) near the top of the cloud. Air is entering the cloud through the sides of the cloud at all levels. The upward motion is actually greater than the horizontal speed, which is the reverse of what is found in larger-scale atmospheric circulations.

The *mature* stage (Fig. 3-34b) begins when rain falls out of the cloud base, and usually lasts for 15-30 minutes. During this stage, the size of drops and ice crystals in the clouds grows so large that the updrafts can no longer support them and they begin to fall as large drops or hail. The frictional drag

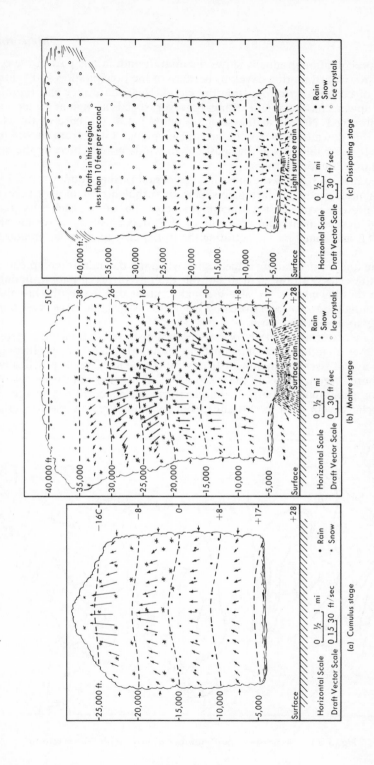

Fig. 3-34. **Life cycle of a cumulonimbus cell.**

of the precipitation gradually slows the updraft and, in one part of the cell, a strong downward motion develops because of the precipitation and "entrainment" of cooler air from outside the cloud. Near the center and top of the cloud, upward motion is still strong, however; speeds as high as 70 mph have been observed. Note also the strong outflow below the base of the cloud. When this downdraft meets the ground it spreads away from the thunderstorm. It is for this reason that gusty, cool winds usually precede the actual arrival of a thunderstorm.

The mature stage is the most intense period of the thunderstorm. Lightning is most frequent during this period, turbulence is most severe, and hail, if present, is most often found in this stage. The cloud reaches its greatest vertical development near the end of this stage, usually reaching above 40,000 ft and sometimes penetrating the tropopause to altitudes greater than 60,000 ft.

The final or *dissipating* stage begins when the downdraft has spread over the entire cell. With the updraft cut off, the rate of precipitation diminishes and so the downdrafts are also gradually subdued. Finally, the last flashes of lightning fade away and the cloud begins to dissolve, perhaps persisting for a while in a stratified form.

Thunderstorms generally occur within moist, warm (maritime tropical) air masses that have become unstable either through surface heating or forced ascent over mountains or fronts. In the United States, practically the only source region of this air mass is the Gulf of Mexico and Caribbean. Note how the geographic pattern of thunderstorm incidence shown in Fig. 3-35 is correlated with both the distance from the source region and topography.

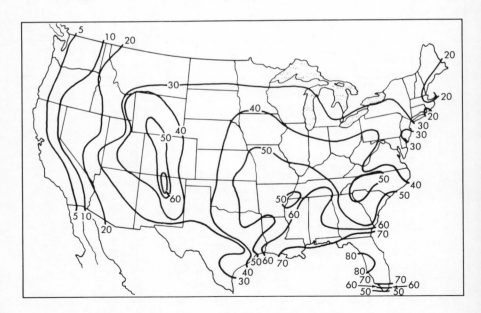

Fig. 3-35.   **Average annual number of days with thunderstorm.**

PROBLEMS

1. In terms of density, explain how a balloonist is able to ascend or descend at will. Before light gases such as helium were available, balloonists inflated their balloons with hot air. What does this show about the effect of temperature on density and thus buoyancy? Why does smoke rise? Explain how portions of the atmosphere acquire buoyancy.

2. How would you classify the mean or standard lapse rate in the atmosphere as far as stability is concerned?

3. Plot a graph having as the abscissa, temperature over the range of +30°C to −55°C; and ordinate, height over the range 0 to 16 km. On the right-hand vertical scale, indicate the standard pressure in the vertical, as determined from Appendix 3 and Fig. 1-1. Plot the following three temperature-pressure soundings measured in three different air masses, by connecting consecutive points in each sounding with straight-line segments. Label each curve. Draw several straight, sloping lines on the chart to illustrate the rate at which temperature changes with height during a dry adiabatic process, one starting at sea level and 30°C, another at 0°C and sea level, and a third at −30°C and sea level.

   (a) Identify layers in the three soundings that exemplify absolutely stable, absolutely unstable, and neutral stratifications.

   (b) Identify all layers containing either an inversion or isothermal lapse rate.

   (c) Where would you say the tropopause is located in the first two soundings?

Air Mass:	*Tropical*	*Polar (summer)*	*Polar (winter)*
Pressure (mb)	*Temp. (°C)*	*Temp. (°C)*	*Temp. (°C)*
1,000	27	13	−31
950	22	13	−32
900	25	9	−32
850	22	4	−30
800	20	−1	−30
700	13	2	−28
600	6	−8	−31
500	−1	−17	−38
400	−13	−32	
300	−28	−50	
200	−50	−50	
150	−51	−50	

4. Compute the height of the base of a cumulus cloud formed by a thermal, if the surface temperature and dew point are 85°F and 49°F, respectively.

Chapter 4

Weather Forecasting

Accurate prediction is the goal of all scientists. But few physical scientists have a more complex, more frustrating, or more challenging medium to work with than does the meteorologist. It has been pointed out in previous chapters that circulations of almost all sizes exist in the atmosphere, that the earth's surface is not only "corrugated" but is covered with different materials, and that even the constituents of the air, especially that very important one, water vapor, vary considerably, in both space and time. With such intricate and ever-changing weather patterns that can be only very inadequately observed, it is little wonder that improvements in the accuracy of prediction have been painfully slow.

Weather forecasting starts with atmospheric observations. More than 10,000 land stations and hundreds of ships take regular "surface" observations, and more than 100 land and sea stations make regular radiosonde observations. In addition, aircraft take observations over oceanic areas where ship reports are scarce, especially in zones where hurricanes form. Through international accord, all the nations of the world exchange their information, except in time of war. To facilitate communication a standard weather reporting code has been adopted.

WEATHER MAP ANALYSIS

After the forecast offices of each country receive the data, the first step is to prepare a three-dimensional analysis of the atmosphere. There are many techniques for studying the variation of atmospheric properties in both the horizontal and vertical, but the most widely used method is the construction of a series of charts that represent horizontal cuts of the atmosphere from sea level to above the tropopause. The so-called *sea level chart* is by far the most complete, both in terms of the number of stations reporting and the number of variables represented at each point. This is the familiar weather map that appears in many newspapers. Examples of surface weather maps are given in Fig. 4-1. At the location of each reporting site, its complete observation is plotted, following the model shown in Appendix 4. A vast

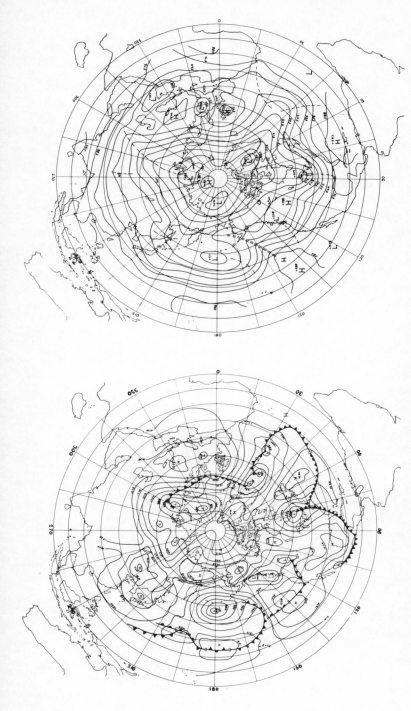

Fig. 4-1. A sequence of sea level and 500-mb (approximately 18,000 ft) charts for the entire hemisphere. Sea level charts: cold front ▲▲▲▲ ; warm front ▲▲▲▲ ; occlusion ▲▲▲▲ ; solid lines are isobars labeled in millibars. 500-mb charts: Solid lines are contours labeled in tens of meters. Heavy dashed lines mark the troughs or "gulleys" of the pressure surface.

97

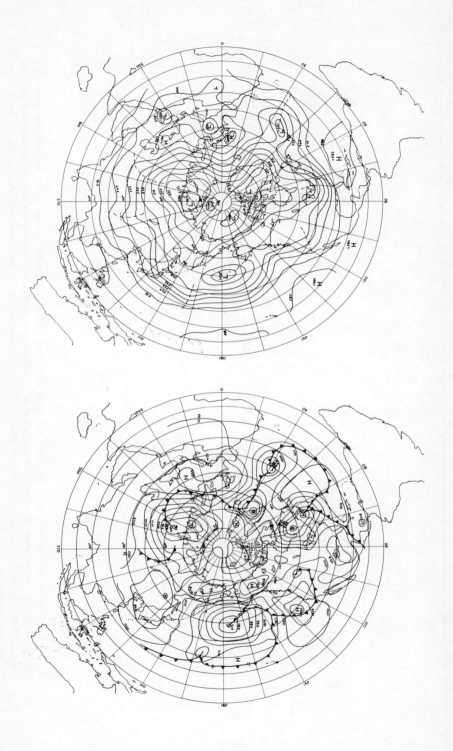

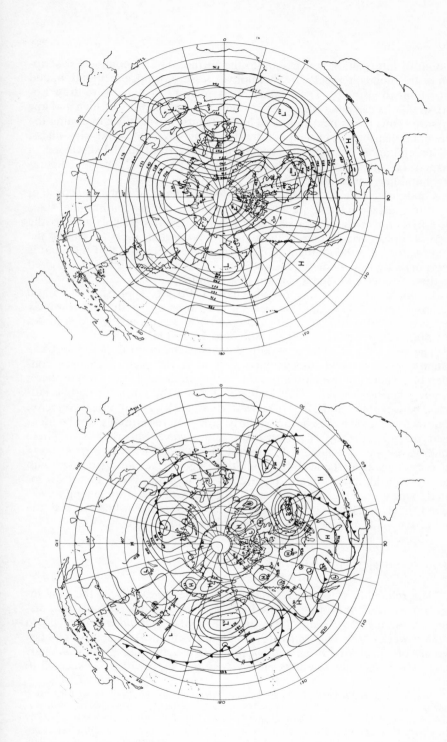

99

amount of information is packed into the surface data: a complete description of the clouds, temperature, humidity, pressure, wind, precipitation, and restrictions to visibility. The weather chart analyst's first step is to draw isobars so that he can determine the position, size, and intensity of high and low pressure centers. His next step is to locate fronts; this he does by noting the horizontal distribution of temperature, humidity, pressure, wind, cloudiness, and precipitation, taking into account the polar front model discussed in Chap. 3. He will also confirm his surface analysis by a study of the temperature, humidity, and wind flow aloft.

Conditions aloft are usually represented by charts of isobaric (constant pressure) surfaces. These are equivalent to charts of constant altitude, since the horizontal pressure gradient at a constant level is proportional to the slope of an isobaric surface (Figure 3-2). On constant pressure charts, the wind conforms to the gradient of contours in the same way that the wind is determined by isobars on a constant altitude chart. The plotting model used for these "upper-air" charts is given in Appendix 5.

Examples of analyzed upper-air charts (500 mb, approximately 5,500 m) are given in Fig. 4-1a. The constant-pressure surfaces that are routinely analyzed are 850, 700, 500, 300, 200, and 100 mb (approximate altitudes of 1,500, 3,000, 5,500, 9,200, 11,800, and 16,200 m).

The sea level chart is generally dominated by several closed isobaric systems—cyclones and anticyclones—but aloft the picture changes considerably. There are few closed systems in the middle and upper troposphere; rather, a general westerly flow undulates around the poles. In middle latitudes, between 40° and 50°, these westerlies usually attain a peak velocity. Four or five major waves in the westerly flow pattern normally can be identified around a hemisphere, with many minor waves superimposed. These small waves are associated with the fast-moving, short-lived (3 or 4 days) wave cyclones near the surface, while the longer waves are associated with the larger-scale, more sluggish features of the weather. When an area is located to the east of the crest and west of the valley of one of these long waves, there is likely to be a 2- or 3-week period of dry weather, while if it is to the east of the valley, wet weather is likely to prevail for a few weeks.

FORECASTING TECHNIQUES

The reliability of weather forecasts decreases markedly as the time interval over which they are projected increases, and so it is customary to distinguish among *short-range* (less than 48 hours), *extended-range* (up to about a week), and *long-range* (up to about a month*) forecasts. The last two are often referred to as *outlooks* and are usually quite general in character. The long-range forecasts merely state that the weather is expected to

---

* Of course, publishers of almanacs and calendars do not hesitate to forecast a year or more in advance and there are a few private weather forecasters who will undertake to forecast the weather many months away. However, their accuracy is generally not above that obtained from "climatology," i.e., from predicting random variations of the average or normal weather, and if they have some scientific method, it is a well-guarded secret.

be colder or warmer, more rainy or less rainy than normal for the area and time of year.

Several techniques have been employed in short-range forecasting, but only the two most widely used methods will be discussed here. The first of these involves the use of rules and formulae to determine the displacement and changes in intensity of such weather map features as lows, highs, fronts, waves aloft, and the jet stream. Because this method directs its efforts at specific prominent features of the weather map, rather than taking into account the complete field of temperature, moisture, and momentum, the accuracy that can be achieved is limited. This technique depends greatly on highly idealized models of atmospheric phenomena, such as that of the wave cyclone discussed in Chap. 3. But characteristic lines and points such as fronts and cyclone centers do not conserve their properties with time; they are affected strongly by an environment that tends to become ever more extensive as time goes on.

The extrapolation of prominent characteristics in the weather pattern is still the most generally used forecasting method. After the weather forecaster has decided on what the weather maps 24 to 48 hours later will look like—where the high and low centers, fronts, etc., will be located, and how intense they will be—he is still faced with the problem of relating the forecast pattern to the minutiae of "weather": exactly where will there be precipitation, and what type? Where will the clouds be and what will be the temperature over New York? To forecast these things, the meteorologist considers the factors that are likely to produce modifications in the idealized models that he has employed. For example, he must estimate whether the heating by a surface or the forced ascent of flow over a hill will be sufficient to release instability that may cause showers in an otherwise clear air mass.

Prediction from Equations

Meteorologists have long dreamed of being able to compute the future state of the atmosphere much as the astronomer computes a future eclipse. The basic physical equations governing the behavior of fluids have been known for almost a century and they have been applied to the atmosphere for over 50 years. In principle, meteorologists should be able to solve these equations to provide weather forecasts. But early attempts to do this ended in dismal failure, and only recently (since about 1949) have practical, although as yet imperfect, computed forecasts been made on a regular basis. There have existed several obstacles to obtaining completely physical-mathematical prognoses:

First, the mathematical equations that describe fluid motion are of a type that cannot be solved simply; so-called numerical techniques, which are extremely laborious, requiring an immense number of computations, must be used. Until the invention of high-speed computers, it was impossible to do these in a reasonable time. Second, observations exist in insufficient detail over much of the earth to permit an accurate representation of the fluid motion everywhere. Meteorologists have had to confine their solution to areas where there is a reasonable density of reports. But, of course, this introduces errors that gradually increase with time, because no portion of the atmosphere can be considered completely independent of the rest. (In other words, the weather 1,000 miles away may provide the "seed" for to-morrow's weather.) Third, most of the time the *net* force acting on any part of the atmosphere is very small compared to each of the *individual* forces acting on it. For example, in the vertical, the force of gravity acting downward on 1 g of air is about 980 dynes; but the vertical pressure gradient force acting upward is also very nearly 980 dynes. This means that to compute the *net* force in the vertical, which may be only 1 or 2 dynes, one must measure the vertical pressure gradient everywhere with a very high degree of accuracy; considering techniques and density of measurement, this is impossible. Fi-nally, there are physical difficulties, such as how to take into account the highly variable effects of friction, mountain barriers, and the distribution of heat and cold sources.

By making certain simplifications in the equations, giant computers now produce forecasts of the fields of horizontal and vertical motion on a routine daily basis. Despite the simplifying assumptions, the results are at least equal to those produced by the older, more subjective methods. Although meteor-ologists are still a long way from producing a weather almanac for long periods of time in advance, numerical prediction is a major step ahead in the science.

Extended- and Long-Range Forecasts

Extended-range forecasting is most commonly accomplished through analysis of the slowly-changing, large-scale features of the atmospheric cir-culation. By averaging the daily charts at various levels over several days, the smaller, fast-moving "eddies" and waves in the flow are suppressed and only the persistent large-scale features remain. Apparently, these big undulations of the averaged flow determine to a great extent the character of the weather over a week or two, just as the migratory wave cyclones produce many of the day-to-day changes at middle and high latitudes.

For forecasts beyond 30 days, all present methods are based on statisti-cal analysis. The search for periodicities (cycles) in weather elements seems to be a favorite occupation of many amateurs and professionals. But aside from the well-known diurnal and annual cycles caused by the earth's move-ments, none seems to be very reliable for forecasting. Another technique that is used is that of *analogues*; it consists of looking for weather patterns from past records that resemble the present one and then forecasting the present situation to evolve in the future in the same way as did the analogous one in the past. Until more is learned about what controls the average large-scale flow in the atmosphere—the general circulation—long-range forecast-ing cannot have a solid physical foundation.

PROBLEMS

1. Identify the major crests and valleys at 500 mb in Fig. 4-1. How do the sea level cyclones and anticyclones move in relation to the large-scale wave pat-terns?

2. Determine the speed and direction of displacement of each wave cyclone on the sea level charts of Fig. 4-1.

3. Is the complexity of the frontal analyses on the sea level charts greater over the oceans or over the continents? Why should there be a difference?

4. Examine the latest weather map published in your local newspaper. Predict whether there will be precipitation (and, if so, the type) and what the temperature, wind, and cloudiness will be at your city 24 hours from the time of the map. List the factors you took into account in predicting each element.

5. Some proverbs state that physical appearance of certain insects and animals is an indication of future weather. Do you doubt their validity? Why?

Chapter 5

Climate

A simple definition of climate is *average state of the atmosphere*. Perhaps it would be better to say that climate describes an imaginary composite of weather, since not only averages but also variations from the averages are significant factors of climate. The diurnal, day-to-day, and seasonal weather changes are as much a characteristic of climate as is the average weather.

The major factors that control climate are, of course, the same that produce weather: (1) The intensity of solar radiation, which is a function of latitude; (2) the reflectivity (albedo) of the earth's surface; (3) the distribution of land and sea; (4) topography. Many local influences affect the small-scale or *microclimate:* vegetation characteristics, small bodies of water such as lakes, and even human activity that alters the surface properties or the purity of the air.

The task of describing and classifying climate is not an easy one, because there are so many facets of the weather that affect human activity. However, the temperature and the water supply are the chief parameters that control the broad-scale distribution of natural and cultivated vegetation. Water supply is dependent on a combination of factors (precipitation, runoff, and evaporation), only two of which—precipitation and evaporation—involve the atmosphere. Evaporation measurements are scanty and unreliable; in any particular area evaporation depends on the type of surface and vegetation, the temperature of the air, the relative saturation of the air, and the winds. As a result, climatologists have either eliminated evaporation from consideration or have attempted to use temperature alone as an index of evaporation.

The average as well as the diurnal and annual variations of temperature are determined principally by latitude, altitude, and the influence of land and sea. Some of these effects can be seen from the average world isotherms of Fig. 2-10. The *latitudinal* variations can perhaps be seen more clearly from Table 5-1.

The mean temperature decreases, the range increases with latitude. But the difference in the percentage of land mass in the two hemispheres also shows up clearly. The average annual range for the Southern Hemisphere, which not only has less land mass but has it concentrated in the tropics, is

104

Table 5-1.   Mean Annual Temperature and Range as a Function of Latitude

Latitude	Mean Temperature (°F)		Mean Annual Range (°F)	
90-80°	—	(−5)*	—	—
80-70	13	(10)	60	(57)*
70-60	30	(27)	62	(30)
60-50	41	(42)	49	(14)
50-40	57	(53)	39	(11)
40-30	68	(65)	29	(12)
30-20	78	(73)	16	(12)
20-10	80	(78)	7	(6)
10-0	79	(79)	2	(3)

* Values in parentheses are those of the Southern Hemisphere.

half that of the Northern Hemisphere. The difference between the temperature regimes of stations close to the ocean and those well in the interior of continents is illustrated by Fig. 5-1. Note how annual range increases with distance from the ocean shore, especially from the western shore, because the stations represented are generally within the belt of prevailing westerlies. (Hawaii is an exception.) The range of temperature is an index of what is called the *continentality* of a station. The diurnal temperature range is also dependent on continentality, as can be seen from Fig. 5-2.

The effect of altitude on the temperature range is illustrated by Fig. 5-3. In parts of the elevated southwest, the average difference between day and night temperatures in winter is 33°F, while a few hundred miles to the east the range is about a third less. This effect largely reflects differences in moisture and cloudiness in the two areas. Although on the average, the temperature decreases with altitude, there are special effects of topography and air circulation that cause deviations from the general rule. For example, temperature inversions along the west coast of South and North America at middle and low latitudes are persistent, normal "climatological" features of the temperature distribution. Along the coastal hills, the average temperature is actually slightly warmer at elevations of 1,000 m or so than it is near sea level. Drainage of cold air into low spots in mountainous terrain produces pockets of cold air throughout much of the year. Farmers know this and so plant their frost-sensitive trees and crops along the slopes, leaving the bottom land for hardier plants.

Temperature is of importance not only to the agriculturist. Human comfort is closely related to the body's heat budget. When the body loses heat faster than it is normally produced, or if the body loses heat more slowly than it should, it suffers discomfort and, under extreme conditions, injury or death. There are several factors that determine the body's rate of heat loss, but one is the temperature of its environment. Some idea of the amount of heating or cooling required in the artificial environments that man creates can be obtained by determining the difference between the mean temperature of a day and some arbitrarily defined ideal temperature (say, 65°F). If one adds up all of these temperature differences over, say, a month, the result can be expressed in terms of *degree days,* a measure of how much heating

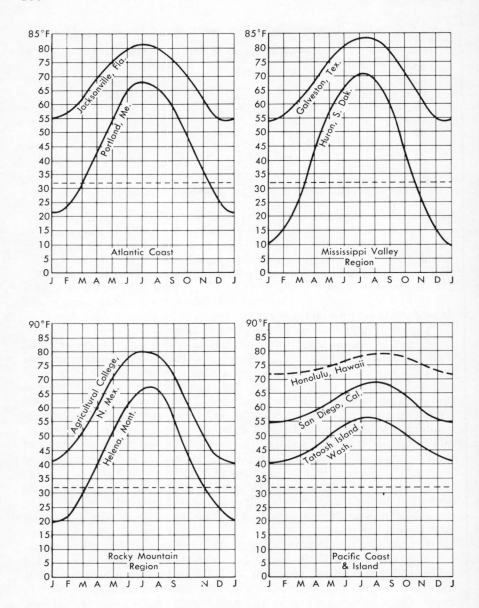

Fig. 5-1. **Annual temperature variation at continental and marine stations.**

or cooling will be needed to achieve ideal conditions. Heating engineers find such information useful in estimating fuel and equipment requirements for any locality. You can obtain a rough estimate of the temperature factors which effect your fuel bill from Fig. 5–4.

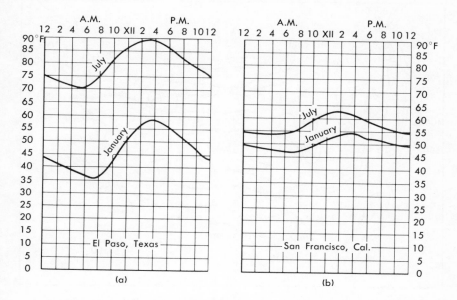

Fig. 5-2. Diurnal temperature variations at (a) a continental and (b) a maritime station.

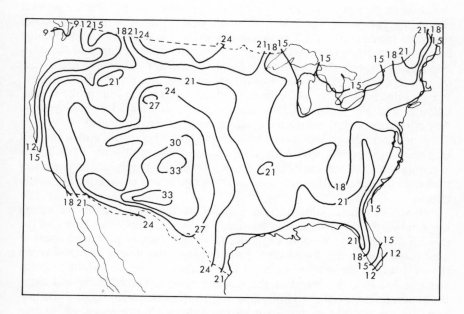

Fig. 5-3. Mean diurnal temperature range (January).

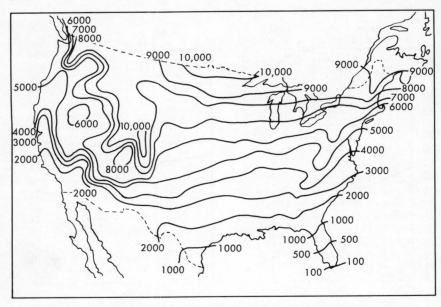

Fig. 5-4.   Heating degree days over the United States (base = 65°F).

Average cloudiness and precipitation are linked most strongly to the general circulation and topography. Figure 5-5 illustrates the latitudinal variation of precipitation, which conforms, approximately, with the general circulation pattern of Fig. 3-19. There is a peak in the doldrums belt where the trade winds converge. The amount drops in the subtropical anticyclone belt, but not drastically. Actually, it is along the eastern edges of the anticyclones in this belt that the great tropical and subtropical deserts are found; the western edges experience upward air motion and ample precipitation. Wave cyclones along the polar front produce much of the rain in the middle latitudes and high latitudes. The polar regions, dominated by anticyclonic flow but experiencing occasional cyclonic weather, are quite arid.

More rain falls on the oceans than on the land (Fig. 5-6), and in the belt of prevailing westerly winds the west coasts of the continents have higher precipitation than the east coasts. Over islands the precipitation is greater than over the surrounding ocean, due to orographic and convective (heating) effects.

Orographic precipitation (that induced by the forced ascent of air on the windward side of mountain barriers) is also an important factor in the rainfall distribution. Notable examples of orographically produced areas of high precipitation are found on the west side of the Rocky Mountains, on the west side of the Andes in central and southern Chile, and along the west coast of Norway. The rains of the summer monsoon over India and along the southern slopes of the Himalayas are greatly intensified by upslope motion. On the lee side of mountain barriers, there are dry areas, called *rain shadows*. Examples of rain shadows are those found to the east of the Cas-

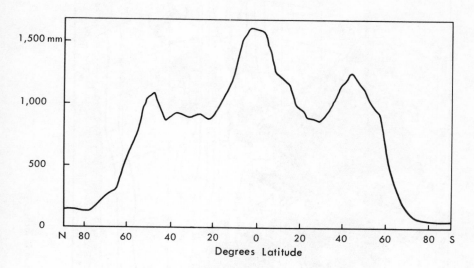

Fig. 5-5. Precipitation as a function of latitude.

cades in the states of Washington and Oregon and the arid Patagonia area in Argentina.

The seasonal distribution of rainfall has great significance, especially for agriculture. Precipitation is much more useful when it occurs during the growing season of plants than when it occurs at other times of the year. There are a great number of seasonal distributions of rainfall. Some of these are shown in Fig. 5-7. Distribution (a) represents the equatorial type. There are two maxima that occur shortly after the equinoxes. The other types are: (b) tropical, (c) monsoon, (d) subtropical (west coast), (e) continental, (f) maritime. The explanation of each distribution is obvious from the names.

CLASSIFICATION OF CLIMATES

The climate of any locality is a composite of many different elements. Only through study of the means, ranges, and diurnal and seasonal variation of the dozens of elements can one obtain a complete picture of the climate. The number of possible combinations of elements and therefore the number of climates is immense. To provide some guidance to climatic conditions of areas, several climatic classification systems have been devised. The most commonly used is that invented by W. Köppen in 1918. Based on annual and monthly mean temperature and precipitation, definitions of climatic types are devised so that areas having approximately the same type of native vegetation fall into one climatic class. Table 5-2 summarizes Köppen's climatic types and definitions. Figure 5-8 shows the world distribution of climate according to this system.

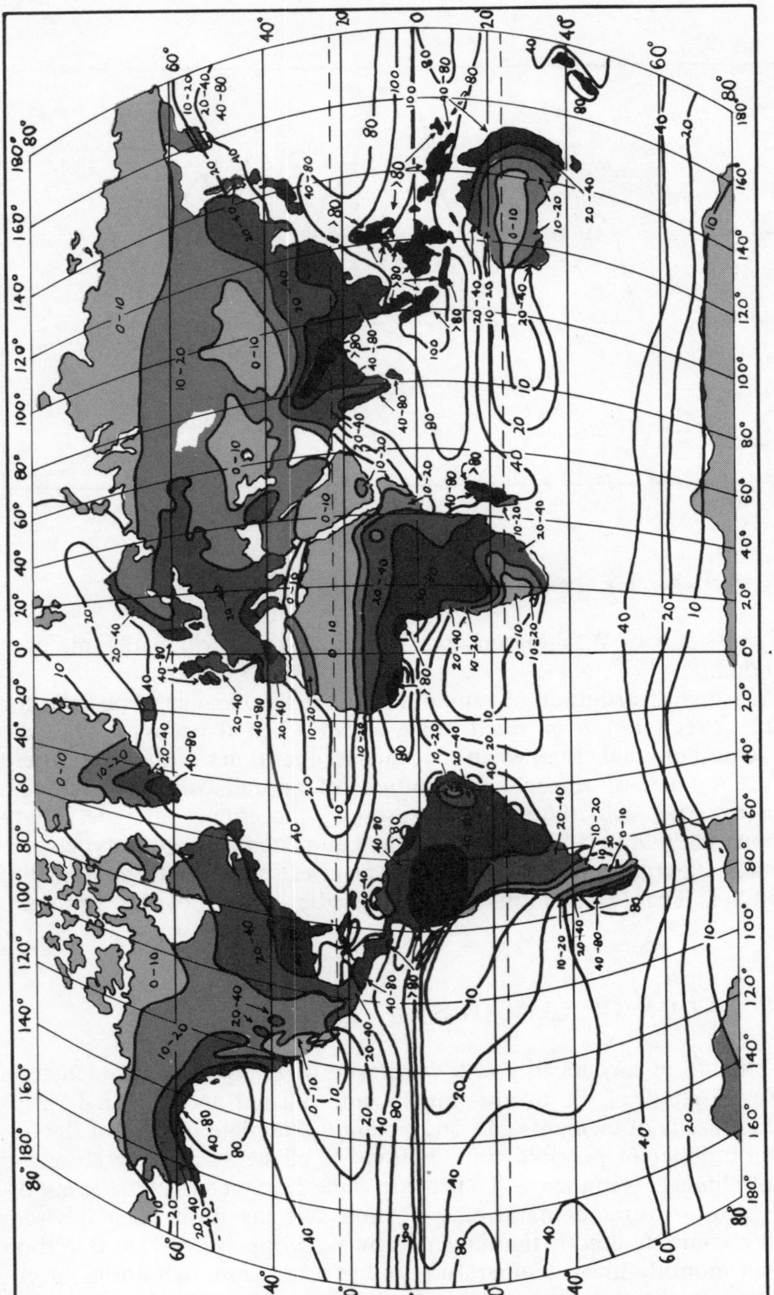

Fig. 5-6. Mean annual precipitation in inches.

110

Table 5-2. Types of Climate

Groups of climate*	Types of climate	Precipitation*
A Tropical rainy (coldest month's temperature > 18°C)	Af, tropical wet	No dry season (driest month > 6 cm)
	Aw, tropical wet and dry	Winter dry season (driest month < 6 cm)
B Dry (evaporation exceeds precipitation)	BS, semiarid (steppe)	
	BSh, tropical and subtropical	Short moist season
	BSk, middle latitude	Meager rainfall, most in summer
	BW, arid (desert)	
	BWh, tropical and subtropical	Constantly dry
	BWk, middle latitude	Constantly dry
C Humid mesothermal (coldest month's temperature between 0° and 18°C)	Cs, dry summer subtropical	Summer drought, winter rain
	Ca, humid subtropical (warmest month > 22°C)	Rain in all seasons
	Cb, marine climate (warmest month < 22°C)	Rain in all seasons, accent on winter
	Cc, marine climate (warmest month < 22°C, less than 4 months > 10°C)	
D Humid microthermal (coldest month's temp. < 0° C; warmest month's temp. > 10°C)	Da, humid continental, warm summer (warmest month > 22°C)	Rain in all seasons, accent on summer; winter snow cover
	Db, humid continental, cool summer (warmest month > 22° C)	Rain in all seasons, accent on summer; long winter snow cover
	Dc, subarctic (less than 4 months > 10°C)	Meager precipitation throughout year
E Polar (warmest month's temp. < 10°C)	ET, tundra	Meager precipitation throughout year
	EF, ice cap	Meager precipitation throughout year
H Undifferentiated highlands		

With A climates:
    f = no dry season; driest month over 6 cm (2.4 in.)
    s = dry period at high sun or summer; rare in A climates
    w = dry period at low sun or winter; driest month under 6 cm (2.4 in)
With C and D climates:
    f = no dry season; difference between rainiest and driest months less than in s and
        w; driest month of summer over 3 cm (1.2 in.)
    s = summer dry; at least 3 times as much rain in wettest month of winter as in driest
        month of summer; driest month less than 3 cm (1.2 in.)
    w = winter dry; at least 10 times as much rain in wettest month of summer as in driest
        month of winter

* Precipitation and temperature values are averages.

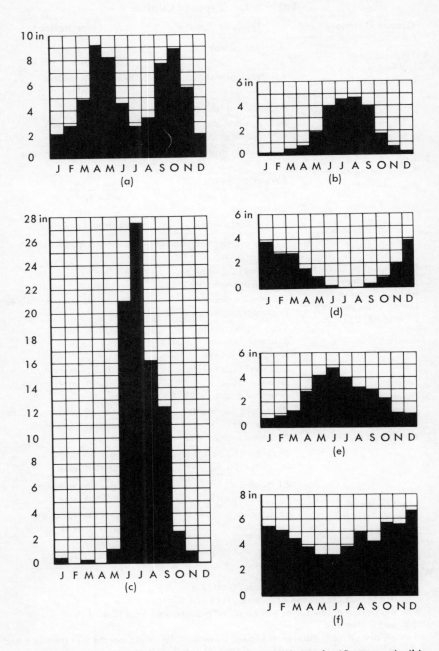

Fig. 5-7. Annual distributions of rainfall: (a) Yaounde (Cameroun), (b) Mexico City (Mexico), (c) Bombay (India), (d) Sacramento (California), (e) Omaha (Nebraska), (f) Valencia (Eire).

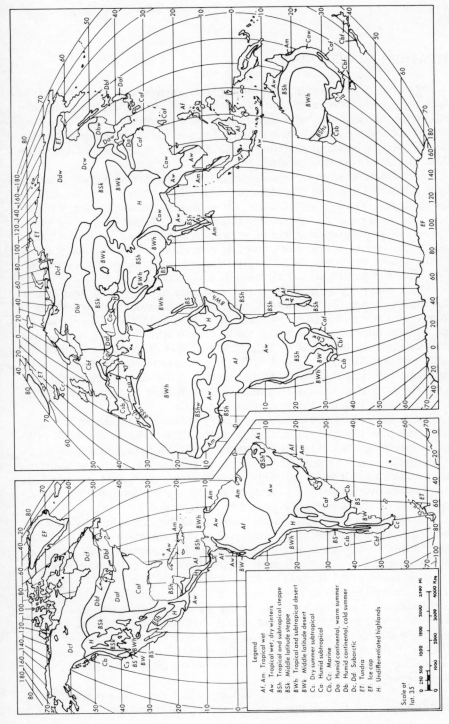

Fig. 5-8. Climates of the world (Köppen).

Legend

Af, Am Tropical wet
Aw Tropical wet, dry winters
BSh Tropical and subtropical steppe
BSk Middle latitude steppe
BWh Tropical and subtropical desert
BWk Middle latitude desert
Cs Dry summer subtropical
Ca Humid subtropical
Cb, Cc Marine
Da Humid continental, warm summer
Db Humid continental, cold summer
Dc, Dd Subarctic
ET Tundra
EF Ice cap
H Undifferentiated highlands

Scale at
lat. 35

0 250 500   1000   1500   2000   2500 Mi

0   1000   2000   3000   4000 Km

WEATHER MODIFICATION

Man has been modifying his atmospheric environment since he first lit fires and moved into caves. But even outside of his shelter, man has been modifying his weather, both intentionally and unintentionally, for a long time. He has done it by changing the contours of the land, changing the surface properties, and contaminating the air. But all of these changes have been done on a relatively small scale.

The different sizes of oscillations of the weather elements must be kept in mind when one considers the feasibility of any particular scheme for deliberate weather modification. On a large or medium scale, we cannot hope, at least in the foreseeable future, to change the climate by inputs of *energy* equaling those of natural atmospheric processes. We could hardly match the rate at which heat energy is converted to kinetic energy (convection) even in a small thunderstorm, and the total rate of energy conversion increases greatly as the circulation size increases.

On a small scale, there are a few examples of the use of heat energy directly to change the weather. Heating of the air over crops to save them from frost damage has been practiced for a long time. Generally, however, the produce must have a fairly high value, such as citrus fruit has, to make the practice economically feasible. During World War II, fog over English airports was sometimes dissipated sufficiently to allow aircraft operations by burning oil to raise the air temperature locally a few degrees above the dew point. In some places sidewalks are kept clear of snow by running hot water or steam pipes beneath the pavement.

Most weather changes that have been produced or proposed are those that result from changes induced in the composition of the air or clouds, or in the surface properties of the earth. One example of a change in surface properties that produces a change in the microclimate is those caused by the extensive areas of asphalt and concrete in a city. Water is often used to control the temperature over crops: On a clear, cold night, the temperature over an irrigated field will be noticeably higher than over dry soil.

Pollutants in the air affect the heat content of the atmosphere by reducing its transparency to the sun's incoming energy and the earth's outgoing heat. Since dust particles serve as condensation nuclei, pollution leads to denser fogs and smogs. Fog is much more frequent over cities than over the surrounding countryside. It may also be that the greater number of nuclei leads to more precipitation over cities.

Modification of clouds by use of dry ice and silver iodide has already been mentioned in Chap. 1. Cloud seeding has not been proved to produce significant changes in precipitation amounts. In fact, it has been much more effective in the *dissipation* of cold (less than 25°F) fogs than as a means for stimulating the rainfall rate. Figure 5-9 shows the effects of seeding a cloud from the air.

Control over the water supply can be achieved in ways other than by increasing precipitation. Suppression of evaporation from lakes and reservoirs

Fig. 5-9.   Cloud deck seeded from the air. (Note the trenches where cloud has been dissipated.)

is one technique that has been employed. This has been done by spreading a monomolecular film of a substance such as cetyl alcohol on the surface of the water. Evaporation can be retarded by 15-20 per cent in this way, but it is difficult to prevent the film from being broken by waves.

Snow is a very important natural "reservoir" of water for many places. If the rate at which snow melts could be controlled, a steady supply of water might be available throughout the year instead of having an overbalance in the spring. Increasing the rate of snowmelt is not too difficult. The high reflectivity of snow can be decreased by covering the surface with some dark material such as lampblack. In Tibet it has long been the practice to throw pebbles on snow fields to speed melting for early planting. But no practical method for retarding snow melt on a large scale has yet been suggested; slowing snowmelt would be immensely valuable to regions such as California, where most of the year's water supply comes in the form of snow over the mountains.

Various proposals have been made for weather modification on a grandiose scale. For example, it has been suggested that large areas of lowlands be flooded to temper the climate of surrounding areas. In northern Siberia the enormous annual temperature range (over 100°F) might be sharply reduced by extensive flooding.

A land bridge across the Bering Strait, cutting off the circulation of waters of the Arctic and Pacific Oceans, has existed in the past, and it has been proposed that this could be rebuilt. This barrier would stop the flow of heat between these bodies of water, presumably raising the temperatures to the south of the strait and increasing the temperature contrast across the barrier.

The question of weather control is a very important one and deserves serious consideration. But until the atmospheric scientist understands atmospheric process more fully and therefore the possible effects that his tinkering may have, he must proceed cautiously. After all, man is very delicately tuned to his existing environment.

PROBLEMS

1. Why is there so much snow and ice over the Arctic and Antarctic even though precipitation is light? Assuming the average precipitation over the Arctic is that of the average at latitude 80°N, what would be the minimum age of the ice at the bottom of a 100-ft. iceberg? (Neglect compression of the snow.)

2. Why does the equatorial type of rainfall distribution have two maxima that occur shortly after the equinoxes?

3. Why does the maximum of precipitation occur in summer over the interiors of continents?

4. Classify the climate of your area of residence according to the Köppen system.

5. Explain the maxima of thunderstorms in Florida and over the Rockies (Fig. 3-35).

6. From a knowledge of the general circulation, deduce the characteristics of the climate of the state of Washington, taking into account the topography.

Units Used in This Book

I. TEMPERATURE SCALES

	Fahrenheit (F)	Centigrade (C)	Kelvin (K) or Absolute (A)
Boiling point of water	212	100	373
Melting point of ice	32	0	273
Divisions between fixed points	180	100	100

Conversion formulas: $\dfrac{^\circ F - 32}{180} = \dfrac{^\circ C}{100}$ $^\circ K = {}^\circ C + 273^\circ$

II. FORCE

British: pound (lb)
Metric: dyne

1 dyne $= 2.2481 \times 10^{-6}$ pounds (lb)
1 pound $= 4.4482 \times 10^{5}$ dynes

III. PRESSURE

lb/in.^{2}; dynes/cm^2; millibar (mb); cm Hg; in. Hg

1 lb/in.^{2} = 68.947 mb = 2.0360 in. Hg = 5.1715 cm Hg = 68,947 dynes/cm^2

1 dyne/cm^2 = 1.4504×10^{-5} lb/in.^{2} = 2.9530×10^{-5} in. Hg
$\quad = 7.5006 \times 10^{-5}$ cm Hg

1 mb = 1,000 dynes/cm^2 = 1.4504×10^{-2} lb/in.^{2} = 2.9530×10^{-2} in. Hg
$\quad = 7.5006 \times 10^{-2}$ cm Hg

1 cm Hg = 13,332.2 dynes/cm^2 = 0.19337 lb/in.^{2} = 13.3322 mb

1 in. Hg = 0.49116 lb/in.^{2} = 33,863.9 dynes/cm^2 = 33.8639 mb

IV. LENGTH

1 meter (m) = 1.093611 yards = 3.2808 ft = 39.370 in.
1 cm = 0.3937 in. = 10^4 microns (μ) = 10^8 angstroms (Å)

V. VELOCITY

1 knot (nautical mile per hour) = 1.1516 statute mph = 0.5148 m/sec
1 mph = 0.8684 knot = 0.447 m/sec
1 m/sec = 2.2369 miles per hour (mph)

VI. ENERGY

1 gram-calorie [or, just "calorie," (cal)]
1 watt-hour = 860 gram-calories (g-cal)
1 British thermal unit (Btu) = 0.293 watt-hour = 251.98 gram-calories

Psychrometric Tables

Table A. Dew Point Temperature (°F) and Saturation Vapor Pressure (in. Hg)

(Pressure = 30 in. Hg)

Air Temperature (°F)	Vapor Pressure (in. Hg)	Depression of Wet Bulb Thermometer (°F)														
		1	2	3	4	5	6	7	8	9	10	15	20	25	30	35
20	0.103	16	12	8	2	−7	−21									
25	0.130	22	19	15	10	5	−3	−15	−51							
30	0.164	27	25	21	18	14	8	2	−7	−25						
35	0.203	33	30	28	25	21	17	13	7	0	−11					
40	0.247	38	35	33	30	28	25	21	18	13	7					
45	0.298	43	41	38	36	34	31	28	25	22	18					
50	0.360	48	46	44	42	40	37	34	32	29	26	0				
55	0.432	53	51	50	48	45	43	41	38	36	33	15				
60	0.517	58	57	55	53	51	49	47	45	43	40	25	−8			
65	0.616	63	62	60	59	57	55	53	51	49	47	34	14			
70	0.732	69	67	65	64	62	61	59	57	55	53	42	26	−11		
75	0.866	74	72	71	69	68	66	64	63	61	59	49	36	15		
80	1.022	79	77	76	74	73	72	70	68	67	65	56	44	28	−7	
85	1.201	84	82	81	80	78	77	75	74	72	71	62	52	39	19	
90	1.408	89	87	86	85	83	82	81	79	78	76	69	59	48	32	1
95	1.645	94	93	91	90	89	87	86	85	83	82	74	66	56	43	24
100	1.916	99	98	96	95	94	93	91	90	89	87	80	72	63	52	37
105	2.225	104	103	101	100	99	98	96	95	94	93	86	78	70	61	48
110	2.576	109	108	106	105	104	103	102	100	99	98	91	84	77	68	57
115	2.975	114	113	112	110	109	108	107	106	104	103	97	90	83	75	65

Table B. Relative Humidity (per cent)

(Pressure = 30 in. Hg)

Air Temperature (°F)	Depression of Wet Bulb Thermometer (°F)														
	1	2	3	4	5	6	7	8	9	10	15	20	25	30	35
20	85	70	55	40	26	12									
25	87	74	62	49	37	25	13	1							
30	89	78	67	56	46	36	26	16	6						
35	91	81	72	63	54	45	36	27	19	10					
40	92	83	75	68	60	52	45	37	29	22					
45	93	86	78	71	64	57	51	44	38	31					
50	93	87	80	74	67	61	55	49	43	38	10				
55	94	88	82	76	70	65	59	54	49	43	19				
60	94	89	83	78	73	68	63	58	53	48	26	5			
65	95	90	85	80	75	70	66	61	56	52	31	12			
70	95	90	86	81	77	72	68	64	59	55	36	19	3		
75	96	91	86	82	78	74	70	66	62	58	40	24	9		
80	96	91	87	83	79	75	72	68	64	61	44	29	15	3	
85	96	92	88	84	80	76	73	69	66	62	46	32	20	8	
90	96	92	89	85	81	78	74	71	68	65	49	36	24	13	3
95	96	93	89	85	82	79	75	72	69	66	51	38	27	17	7
100	96	93	89	86	83	80	77	73	70	68	54	41	30	21	12
105	97	93	90	87	83	80	77	74	71	69	55	43	33	23	15
110	97	93	90	87	84	81	78	75	73	70	57	46	36	26	18
115	97	94	91	88	85	82	79	76	74	71	58	47	37	28	21

Appendix 3

"Standard" Atmosphere

Altitude (m)	Temperature (°C)	Pressure (mb)	Density (kg/m³)
0	15.0	1013.2	1.2255
500	11.8	954.6	1.1677
1,000	8.5	898.7	1.1120
1,500	5.2	845.5	1.0584
2,000	2.0	794.9	1.0068
2,500	− 1.2	746.8	.9572
3,000	− 4.5	701.0	.9094
3,500	− 7.8	657.5	.8634
4,000	−11.0	616.3	.8193
4,500	−14.2	577.2	.7770
5,000	−17.5	540.1	.7363
5,500	−20.8	504.9	.6972
6,000	−24.0	471.6	.6598
6,500	−27.2	440.2	.6240
7,000	−30.5	410.5	.5896
7,500	−33.8	382.4	.5567
8,000	−37.0	355.8	.5252
8,500	−40.2	330.8	.4952
9,000	−43.5	307.2	.4664
9,500	−46.8	285.1	.4388
10,000	−50.0	264.2	.4127
10,500	−53.2	244.6	.3876
10,769	−55.0	234.5	.3747
11,000	−55.0	226.2	.3614
12,000	−55.0	193.4	.3090
13,000	−55.0	165.3	.2642
14,000	−55.0	141.4	.2259
15,000	−55.0	120.9	.1931
16,000	−55.0	103.3	.1651
17,000	−55.0	88.3	.1412
18,000	−55.0	75.5	.1207
19,000	−55.0	64.6	.1032
20,000	−55.0	55.2	.0883
25,000	−55.0	11.5	.0184
30,000	−55.0	5.4	.0078
35,000	−33.0	2.8	.0035
40,000	3.7	1.6	.0017

Plotting Model for Sea Level Weather Chart

WW Symbols

∞ haze
≡ fog
' drizzle
• rain
* snow
   rain shower
   thunderstorm
   snow shower

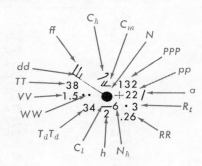

Symbols

		Example
N:	Amount of total sky cover	Overcast
ff:	Barbs show wind speed (full barb = 10 knots)	25 knots
dd:	Arrow shaft shows wind direction	Northwest
TT:	Temperature (°F)	38°F
VV:	Visibility (miles)	1.5 miles
WW:	Weather type	Continuous light rain
T_dT_d:	Dew point temperature (°F)	34°F
C_l:	Type of low clouds	stratus
h:	Height of ceiling	300-599 ft
N_h:	Amount of low cloud cover	6/8
RR:	Precipitation amount, past 6 hours	0.26 in.
W:	Weather, past 6 hours	Rain
R_t:	Time precipitation began or ended	Began 3-4 hours ago
a:	Trend of barograph curve, past 3 hours	Rising
pp:	Pressure change, past 3 hours	+2.8 mb
PPP:	Sea level pressure, with only last three digits (including tenths) given	1,013.2 mb
C_m:	Type of middle clouds	Nimbostratus
C_h:	Type of high clouds	Cirrus

Plotting Model for Upper-Air Chart

Symbols	Example
dd: Arrow shaft shows wind direction	270°
ff: Barbs show wind speed (triangle, 50 knots; full barb, 10 knots)	65 knots
TT: Temperature (°C)	5.3°C
T_dT_d: Dew point temperature (°C)	−1.6°C
hhh: Height of pressure surface (in meters), with only last three digits given	1,558 m (850 mb surface)

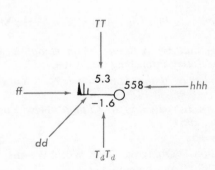

Bibliography

Elementary books on general meteorology and climatology

Battan, Louis J., *The Nature of Violent Storms*. Garden City, N.Y.: Doubleday & Co., Inc., 1961.

Blair, Thomas A. and Robert C. Fite, *Weather Elements*. Englewood Cliffs, N.J.: Prentice-Hall, Inc., 1965.

Blumenstock, David Irving, *The Ocean of Air*. New Brunswick, N.J.: Rutgers University Press, 1959.

Brooks, C. E. P., *Climate in Everyday Life*. New York: Philosophical Library, Inc., 1951.

Dobson, G. M. B., *Exploring the Atmosphere*. New York: Oxford University Press, 1963.

Hare, F. K., *The Restless Atmosphere*. New York: Harper & Row Publishers, Inc., 1963.

Mason, Basil J., *Clouds, Rain and Rainmaking*. New York: Cambridge University Press, 1962.

Neuberger, Hans and F. B. Stephens, *Weather and Man*. Englewood Cliffs, N.J.: Prentice-Hall, Inc., 1948.

Petterssen, S., *Introduction to Meteorology*. New York: McGraw-Hill Book Co., Inc., 1958.

Riehl, Herbert, *Introduction to the Atmosphere*. New York: McGraw-Hill Book Co., Inc., 1965.

Spar, Jerome, *Earth, Sea, and Air. A Survey of the Geophysical Sciences*. Reading, Mass.: Addison-Wesley Publishing Co., 1965.

Sutton, O. G., *The Challenge of the Atmosphere*. New York: Harper & Bro., 1961.

Trewartha, Glenn T., *An Introduction to Climate*. New York: McGraw-Hill Book Company, Inc., 1954.

Some sources of weather data

The Smithsonian Institution, Washington, D.C. "World Weather Records"

U.S. Weather Bureau (ESSA), Washington, D.C.:
   Average Monthly Weather Resume and Outlook
   Climates of the States
   Climatic Charts for the United States
   Climatological Data for the U.S. by Sections
   Daily Weather Map
   Monthly Climatic Date for the World

   (In addition, the U.S. Weather Bureau publishes many pamphlets on particular meteorological phenomena.)

Index